NOT MANY NOBLE

A story of the Lanarkshire Coalfield

Robert L. Aitken

Published by
THE OLD MUSEUM PRESS

NOT MANY NOBLE

First published by The Old Museum Press Limited
The Old Museum, Bramber, West Sussex BN44 3WE
England
1998

A catalogue record of this book
is available from The British Library

Cover design. Setting and format by StewART

ISBN 1 84042 026 X

Printed and bound in Great Britain by
Biddles Limited, Guildford & Kings Lynn

CONTENTS

ACKNOWLEDGEMENTS

National Coal Board - Archives and Miners.

Edinburgh. National Library and Maps Dept.

Edinburgh Central Library.

Library Staff at Bathgate and West Calder.

Paul Archibald Lanark Library, Kate McManus.
Forth Library.

Migration and Emigration - Dilineation of Scotland-
1791-Heron.

Scottish Emigration - T.M Devine.

Scotland's Story - T Steel.

West Calder Society - J McKay.

Shale Oil Scotland - D Kerr.

Kind people all over the district whose
help have been invaluable.

Reminiscences of Haywood. Geo Donaldson.

Romance of Wilsontown. P.M Ritshie.

Scottish Miners.

AUCHENGRAY

Oh since I joined the army
I have travelled far and wide
And I've seen some bonny sights that
Justify the English pride
But though England has some bonny toons
And bonny country tae
There's nae place this side the border
Tae compare wi' Auchengray.

Oh London I am bound to say
Is an interesting toon
Wi' nought but bonny sights in't
For a guid twa - three miles roon
But it's artificial beauties
That took such a lot to pay
Canna staun beside the heather
Tae be seen at Auchengray.

Just thrice as yet I've had the chance
Tae tak' a daunner roon
And see the sights o' London
That great and famous toon
When I saw the Hoose O' Parliament
I to myself did say
Within that hoose some day will sit
A man frae Auchengray.

And there's no much wrang wi' Bedford
A better place you couldna choose
Situated on the banks
Of the grand old river Ouse
But for a' it's Picture Palaces
And shops in grand array
This cheil' wad raither be back in
That wee place - Auchengray.

Oh some folk say oor village
Is the place that God made
But i'm sure these people never say
the mud of Biggleswade
And though it's a more modern toon
Getting better day by day
It will never come up' - sides
Wi' that village -Auchengray.

Then take Norwich also
That'a fine auld English toon
But its no the kinna place where
I'd tak' hoose and settle doon
For although I didn't know it
Until I came away
No place in England is as dear
to me as Auchengray.

It doesn't matter where I go
Bedford, Norwich or Haynes Park,
Biggleswade or London,
France, Belgium, or Denmark:
Be it e'er so far away
There'll ne'er be ony fears
O'me forgetting where I lived
For my first 18 years.

CHAPTER ONE
THE STRANGER'S VIEWPOINT.

The stranger stood at the high point of the village. The Pentland Hills, away in the distance made a fitting background this sunny morning. The early sun had chased the night shades away and it seemed a sacrilege to think of darkness at such a moment.

Allermuir, Caerketton and Scald Law stood proudly; at ease, at one, with the warmth of the air and the blue of the sky; their train of hills following their lead light round the picture, taking in the highlands of Biggar. This range of hills was concluded by the broad dome of Tinto. At its most westerly it was partly hidden by a nearer smaller mound.

The young lady had an excellent view facing south, but I saw as I approached, that the panorama of hills and moorland was not engaging her attention. I had left my car down at the entrance to the village, and I was surprised to see anyone at this lonely spot; especially as there was no car where I had left mine.

She was unaware of my approach. It was a grassy slope up which I strolled, and soft underfoot, it only whispered a protest in response at my trespass. Her attitude took my attention away from contemplation of the hills. She was not seeing far horizons, but leaning against a small iron railing of four bars was intent on reading the information contained in lead lettering on a small granite slab.

Yet she gave the impression, as I stood for a moment, that she was seeing far more than fourteen names on a monument, slowly warmed in the dew of the morning; eleven from world war one and three from the second.

The place was well known to me, my special place of pilgrimage, where I had spent my childhood. I had retained throughout all those years, the memory of sights and sounds of long ago; a corner of my heart for this lonely spot which was not, nor ever just a point on a map.

As I approached, not desiring to disturb and frighten this young visitor I coughed quietly to herald my presence. She turned quickly at the sound, and I saw tears stand in her eyes before she hastily wiped them away with the back of her hand. Soon she was blowing her nose with her handkerchief, while she rapidly regained her composure.

She was as surprised as I had been, earlier, when I spied the lonely figure. Her reaction was quick and rather brusque.

"I never saw you when I came up here. I never even heard you. What are you doing here?"

"May I repeat your question? What are you up here for?" - a draw but she did not seem to be satisfied, and looked fit and willing to carry on into extra time. I was prepared as well, but she was quicker off the mark, to take up the argument.

"I have a right to be here. What right have you?" My reply was succinct.
"It's a free country, and there is no law of trespassing in these moors". She interrupted me. "I have not come here out of mere curiosity. I'm here as the fulfilment of a promise made to my grandfather before he died. I have come a long way to get

here". I could barely stop her flow as I asked her. "Where have you come from, and what are you doing in this lonely place?" I thought there must have been a sense in which I reckoned this as private ground and not available to strangers. Perhaps she felt this in the tone of my voice.

"I have come a long way to get here this morning. It has been a long journey. I left Edinburgh very early and got off at a small station; West Calder was its name. I had bother finding someone to bring me here and when I did succeed he had never heard of the place. Fortunately I had bought an Ordnance Survey Map so we were able to follow the road. He got on all right till we had to turn off the main road. He was not too happy about coming any further, but he was prepared to go on as long as there was a road. Was I glad to get here at last? I told him my errand and asked him to wait; he would not wait the hour at least I wanted, and asked for his money. When he told me the fare I was tempted to go back with him; but this would have defeated the purpose of the visit. His ears were ringing when he left, but I am sure that the thirty pounds I handed over must have sweetened him for he grabbed it and ran; with the money. I have heard stories of mean Scots, and I think that will be sufficient for me to believe it". I finally managed to halt her at this point.

"How are you getting back to Edinburgh" I queried.

"I will walk to the nearest village. There was one just along from where we turned off the main road. Perhaps I will get a bus there". She had not asked me from which town or village I had come, so I never ventured the information although by this time she must have seen my car at the foot of the hill; neither did I satisfy her about a lift home, although I had come from Edinburgh. She was a stubborn lady and certainly was not going to demean herself by asking any favours from another

10

mean Scotsman. I did not keep her in suspense, but took her up on the small matter of Edinburgh.

"You don't speak like someone from the capital? Is it Australia or New Zealand"?

"I see I will need to tell you my story. My name is Elizabeth Manson. My grandmother left the village at the end of the world war. She was unmarried at the time and she managed to get a passage with another family. She was not the only one of the family to emigrate. Another branch settled in Canada. I do not know much about them.

She married the man who was to be my grandfather and I am of that line".

I broke into her spiel when she took a breath. "How would you like to stay here now?"

"I have stayed all my life in New Zealand and if this morning is anything to go by you can count me out as an expatriate. Imagine coming here to live after my home country; no chance. A short visit will do me."

This made the opening I had been looking for, so once again I cut her short. It was time for me to say something in defence of my native land, and especially a wee village the whereabouts of which were unknown to a man living no more than twelve miles away.

"Look up," I said. "Be like the psalmist! to the hills will lift my eyes. Let me point out some landmarks for you that would be familiar to your granny".

I then proceeded to name the peaks of the Pentlands and stretching all the say to Coulter Fell and Tinto hill. I was on my hobby horse and we sat down while I told her of the real experience of walking these same hills. "Put on your walking boots. Take it easy the first time. Got to Hillend ski slope and step out to Allermuir; that is the peak nearest Edinburgh. You must not go back to your own land without seeing the best of mine. You will stand on the top of Scotland's royal city. Or if that is too strenuous for your first hike, take the bus to Holyrood and walk along past St Margaret's loch and up the brae to Dunsapie loch. From there, this is an easy path to the top of Arthur's Seat. You will not only see the town from a different angle but you will see the famous Firth of Forth with its famous bridges, with the Lomond Hills for a backdrop. Sweep round and measure in your mind the distance to Berwick Law or Bass Rock, and May Island away in the distance.

What about going to Flottersone then over the hills to Balerno and The Threapmuir reservoir via Glencorse then back across the hills to Silverburn. A day like this would be ideal for a walk from one end to the other from Allermuir in the east to Byrehope Mount and down via West Water reservoir to West Linton."

She interrupted me. "Could I have some leaves out of your note book to take down some of this information, because I will never remember it when I get home?" She went on to say; "why this place so far away from your home."

I had her undivided attention. "I have a reason for this pilgrimage as well as you. My story is not as bad as yours maybe, but it is as real. I was not born here. My family came here when I was one year old. It must have been a sad year for my parents. They lost two sons; one older than I by a year and the other younger by 2 years but my sadness today is not of the unremembered years but events earlier and later." She caught my mood.

12

"Yes it really is a forlorn place, and near at hand it looks most desolate. There does not seem to be any life around except a few farms and isolated cottages. This is not the thriving mining village described by my grandfather. He talked of a large village. I can see only one away to our left. What is that small reddish hill just beside it? Then there are a few houses round to the middle. Here there is nothing but grasses and reeds and not very green except around the immediate area."

Why she should be so persistent in declaring its ugliness and bareness I did not know, but she had captured my feelings, and my attention. My reading that morning had had some sombre overtones. In the Scotsman, two articles carried were applicable to the present situation. I then told her about my morning reading.

The dispute about a monument to the Duke of Sutherland had been resurrected again. Should it be removed or demolished? Should it be retained? He was not even a Scotsman. Before he married the Countess of Sutherland he had been the Duke of Sheffield. His name will forever be linked with the infamous 'Clearances'. Barbaric and heartless, his name was anathema to all in Scotland and as such should be completely destroyed.

The other argument opposed this view. It should be retained as a constant reminder of a hard hearted despot who valued sheep more than humans. But his effigy still stands on a hillside overlooking Dunrobin Castle-ancestral home of the Sutherlands. Taking in the pillar on which it stands, one hundred and five feet, reputedly built by the same folk who had suffered under the regime. Including the castle it makes a monument to architecture and magnificence. Do all agree? Perhaps on a lovely morning, to the casual visitor it might appear so, but could that be Bein Braghaidh frowning in anger when the clouds hang out their curtains of mourning. At least it seemed to overshadow this great work of man.

The other item of news, relevant to our present circumstance, was of more immediate interest. Concern over the pollution of the rivers of West Lothian from disused mines and other industry. The question raised was simple. Who should take the blame and who should clean up the mess?

There were three candidates in the frame; the owners prior to nationalisation; the National Coal Board; or the present Local Authority.

The N.C.B was history and no longer existed. The private owners in all probability were all dead, so it was felt that our present generation of taxpayers would need to foot the bill.

So we stood there in this deserted village and read together fourteen names on a small marble plinth; eleven from World War I and three from World War II and tried to find some meaning and logic from it all. She crystallised my thoughts. "It seems fitting that it should be placed at this high point; a war memorial and a village dead and buried with creeping threshes and coarse grass covering its dead."

"Look around again and you will see the monument raised in its memory; These slag heaps or bings, pock marking the surrounding neighbourhood. What had been done to keep it alive? Nothing; they knocked down twenty and more rows of houses and used the bricks to build another, nearer the pits that were the lifeline. They created work in abundance for a short time and then moved onto new fields of coal where another generation would subsist until it too died although not yet buried. Unemployment and age would soon accomplish its interment."

"But you said earlier they were poor places for people to live."

"Yes but there are other villages which had boom times as well. The authority here must have felt that the houses; like the workforce were expendable. No attempt was ever made to improve the conditions of the houses, unlike the village with the red bing that you see in the distance," was the only answer I had.

"How did they manage it there? She questioned me.

"They built a scullery on to all the houses and water was piped in, so bathrooms brought them into the twentieth century. These are still occupied and are now owned by many of the folk whose ancestors lived and worked in the shale mines. I do not think any of the original houses have been demolished. Even another area, which had a notorious manager of the four pits nearly had a village that was the envy of all around, because as funds were made available from the substantial profits in the pits some were invested for this purpose.

Going back to the morning in question when the sun had done it's work of chasing the darkness and rising inexorably into the blue sky you had to feel that there was a brighter side to my thoughts. It gave a feeling of permanence. This sun would rise tomorrow; although clouds might obscure the light of the sun, but the earth, and its time dwellers would not be denied its heat and its beneficent effects.

My reverie was halted by my young companion. "Show me the full extent of the village. What about its age and use in the area?"

With this I said. "Come down to the car and I will show you maps of its extent in its heydays". From the maps she saw the approximate location of the rows and their names with special emphasis on the ruins nearby of the house where I had been brought up till I was ten. She noted the names. Enclosed from these early maps were names and streets and rows mentioned in the census roll of 1891. There were twenty three rows or streets. Add nine separate cottages not including farms - five in number. The same census gives the total population as follows; Schedule 1-83=500; 86-163=400; 167-226=300 Total = 1200.

This number as checked against another older calculation, which at best was only a conjecture at 1300, makes the final total correspond. It may be taken for granted that on the day of the census, there would be girls in the family absent for various reasons. Domestic service for girls just left school would be a necessary aspect of home life. Many would go away from the district for this reason. Farm service for girls would be featured, and this too, took away from the real count of local inhabitants. Boys who were not in the pit might have opted for farm service up and down the country. It could well be that at the height of the life of the village this could account for the figure quoted. It never seemed to be higher than this at any subsequent date.

Today it might average the total of 1841 of fifty eight scattered over the whole area.

By the years 1925-35 it had disappeared like 'snow off a dyke'. Only the Stone Rows remained after Loan Street (No 8 Rows.) was demolished. The church and Manse survived, but not for pupil and minister. The church which at one time rang to the singing of the Psalms of David, has been taken over by the night birds; while swallows flit in and out of its ruins by day. At this moment of time the manse is owned privately, and Pentland cottage has just seen its last tenant depart, and it too, along with the rusting body of an old Austin car, is crumbling away to dust and ashes.

16

Nearer to our vantage point there stands the gaunt remains of the pub; a welcome hostelry for bona fide travellers from outside the drink zone on a Sunday.

Other days it was quieter except for Friday and Saturday nights. Now it has been silenced in its desolation. The sheltering roof has fallen in and the storms are set to put the finishing touches to its final life. The doors gape like a skeleton without its teeth; does it call in its impotence for former company? There appears to be a sadness, as it waits for feet to walk through; no cheery fire in the old hearth, with the old oil lamps adding to the comfort of the visitors. The windows; their use long since become redundant, with a gauntness like the eyeholes in a skull; a wildness that comes of despair; in searching for friends that never will return.

Nearer still and far more evocative are the green mounds shrouding another corpse; the house where I spent my childhood; but is there here a slight hint that there is life after death. A small stunted tree grows out of the ruins of an old fireplace. Perhaps it owes its very existence to the ashes of a fire, that; long gone out, helped to make a home out of a room. Perhaps this little parable is saying something consoling. Amidst our own regrets and failures there is still hope. The loss of precious possessions and relationships can be a stunning blow to the spirit. My reveries are interrupted and I raise my eyes a little further away where the threshes grow in abundance.

The football field, shed of its goalposts, and missing the crowds that used to support the team, that made the village proud to be associated with it " I forgot to tell you of another little mound. It lies over against the outline of the pub; the remains of the Gospel hall where my parents worshipped. Nothing is left, but the grass covering the meagre outlines of the foundations, rounding off the same with a symmetry of its own.

The wind soughing through the place brings its own music to make up for the long forgotten voices of the original congregation. Perhaps it is carrying a sweeter and softer edition of the old Sankey hymn; earlier sung without musical accompaniment. It is so, I was there at the last meeting held in the hall. My understanding of the singing was this; it fell far short of the Orpheus Choir.

Before I was old enough to go to the morning service, it was a case of listening for the last hymn, and the sound of movement which heralded dinner time. The word lunch was not known. After this it was time for Sunday School. There were occasions when this was a bore, and the waste of a good summer afternoon.

It was a discipline that never varied, and was a common arrangement for a large majority of the children in those days. Parents would be glad of the hour's respite from the incessant clamour of weans about the house - perhaps the quotation was coined then: 'peace perfect peace'.

The place of worship has moved on; most members even further than that.

The railways have disappeared, but the final demise was not the sole prerogative of Dr. Beeching. The branch was finally closed in the early fifties, but other collieries' lines had ceased to operate long before that. The great strike of 1926 left these obsolete.

Suddenly there is a sound; a whaup (curlew) is calling, not to us but to a nearer relative, telling of our unwanted presence. Humans are scarce and obviously surplus to requirements; better off without us. I was reminded of Hadyn's Creation, and I tried to tell her what I could remember.

18

God made his creatures to produce after their own kind. Over it all he wrote. It is good. There still was no creature to be grateful for his work; to praise him for his goodness, so on the sixth day he made a man in his image and likeness. Male and female created he them. He made us superior to all that had been prepared before hand....is that why He said on that day 'It is very good'! This morning's experience had cast some doubt on that. We had not fulfilled the role for which we had been made.

"The curlew is quite a lonely bird. This is evidenced by its double call, and its landing in this barren place; gliding down some distance from its nest. This is to prevent predators becoming aware of its nest; made more important by the fact its nest lies open to view to careful wanderers, although its eggs blend in with the surroundings.

When I was young they were far more plentiful but the lapwing (peeser) was in abundance. Flocks would wheel and dance about the sky, where they never collided. There was no place for silence when they were above your head.

Peeweep has another meaning in Scotland. It is the word used to describe the dark blue singlet men wore at their work underground. It was made of thin material, but heavy enough in the warm sometimes damp conditions at the coal face. In the early thirties they were sold in packets of six at 7 ½ Pence each.

She seemed keen to hear more about the village and inter-rupted me. "What other birds? There are not many trees; a lot of forests on my way here, but apart from a small stand on that little hill, there are very few." I was quick to answer.

There was always a rookery there. It was called the planting and over behind it lay the station. Notice one or two trees over to the left; they were in the playground of the school.

That is all that is left, except the pillars making the entrance to the girl's and boy's playground.

There were blackbirds nesting in the hedgerows, and in and around the houses. All the farms nearby had their recurring foreign visitors; swallows and their kin from faraway places.

Meadow pippets (mossy) went about their business with the nest tucked in at the foot of a bush, while skylarks their noisier neighbours were more readily seen and heard. The poet got it right 'And singing still dost soar and soaring ever singest.' Can there be a more delightful sight and sound as it rises straight from the ground up and further up, to grace the heavens and fill the air with its song. To me it was always one of the great joys of a summer walk from my early days of stravaiging the fields.

A pair of wagtails had a nest for years in the crevice of a disused bing of an old pit just off the old Crusher railway.

Bird nesting for us was a very private pastime. No thought was ever given to harrying a nest of its young on the eggs. This word means to rob. We kept it from the next of the village. Neither did you visit it too often, or in large numbers we were told: and obeyed. What a disaster it would be; never to know the thrill and wonder as you put your hand lightly into the nest to see if the eggs were warm, and conjecture how long it would be before they hatched. This feeling was indeed compounded, when one day you looked in and saw the first egg chipped. This to be followed shortly by the full brood of four young birds, looking nothing like their parents. Every visit was an experience of excitement and surprise.

There always was a sense of loss to go one day and find the nest flown. We were not sage enough to look to another year; that was too far ahead.

Birds are not so plentiful; not just here but all over the country. The presence and variety - even with the mines going and producing fumes of all kinds, allied to the numerous fires in the homes seemed still to leave room safely for them.

Habitat around this area has not been given over to intensive farming operations, as has been the case in much of rural Britain, but it has suffered its share of pollution and pesticides.. Is it just the nostalgia of looking back?

Later that night I sat at the t.v and watched a programme about the silent skies, and was saddened to learn that many of the songbird population had reduced by more than fifty percent.

There were other kinds of birds that were visitors to our moors in spring and early summer. The cuckoo with its double call, as it looked out from the branches of a tree on the edge of pasture land 'cuckoo-coo'. It was a rivalry among us who could list its call as it was repeated. As it became upset it would continue these twin notes in rapid succession. It might surprise us to know that the female will lay eight to twelve eggs depositing one in each separate nest. Its eggs could vary in colour often mimicking the eggs of its host.

The nests it uses are often wagtails, pipits and warblers. You will find them being pursued by these kind of birds who obviously resent their presence. Yet these same kind of birds will except the cuckoo's egg although distinctly larger than their own, indeed will incubate the egg and rear the young bird at the expense of her own brood. There have been instances where the larger fledgling will get rid of the smaller birds and the mother will continue to feed the interloper.

The skylark might well be deemed the most common kind of the grass and threshes. Indeed it is the most common lark in

Europe. Its singing is the very epitome of the countryside. It has a high pitched - special singing as it rises to great heights. It sings through most of its descent, stopping only when it comes in to land quickly and directly near its nest.

Another favourite was the meadow pipit (Moss cheeper or the abbreviation (mossy). It shared its territory with the lark and nested where there was protection in long grass; nest well hidden at the foot of a bush. Like the lark it also sings in its ascent but could never be mistaken for its more famous kin.

To listen to the drumming of the snipe was a sure sign that a nest was near. It flies with swiftness that accentuates its shape. It nests in marshes and moors; its nest similar to other wading birds. This is a hollow scraped out and lined with grass.

We were fortunate to have the presence of the elusive corncrake. The call like its name was quite distinct from all other birds, but a sight of it was a very rare occurrence, as it retreated further into cover when approached.

"But that is enough about birds" I replied "It is your turn. Is not the history of all countries much the same? Barbarity and starvation causing people to move to other places".

"Going back to our talk, that was not all I read this morning. An older story than yesterdays news, it was the age old story of a lonely crowded roadside outside a city gate; a man bowed beneath the weight of a heavy cross, urged on by a crowd out of control, at the incitement of the leaders of the nation. Was this not desolation among a crowd?

Do we hear a friendly shout among the rabble? Not one; it was sheer murder of a man who was God. What have been the results of this monstrous act? The answer lies in our own

22

hearts. Are we worthy of this sacrifice? Surely it merits a mention of worth in the middle of past scenes of last century.

Calvary.

No clash of steel on this great battlefield;
No cleaving of helmeted skull by sword's edge keen.
But oh I forget there is a noise of steel on steel.
Hammer hitting nails through unprotesting flesh.
No mailed fist is raised in anger by this non combatant:
No shout of defiance, nor yet a plea for self.
What will he offer for it all?
Father forgive they know not what they do.
Tis always victors from their vantage point
Write history, and thereafter tell the tale.
Not there at Calvary's uneven defeat;
For now the vanquished wears the royal wreath,
And as such will write his story o'er and o'er
In human hearts and lives from shore to shore; until
The meek shall inherit not just the earth but heaven as well,
Because the meekly king was crowned with thorns
And at the last; Sword's hateful plunge
Drew forth the blood to save.

"But that was not the last of that story,"she hastily replied.
"He rose again. I have a story to tell you, but there is a
different ending. If you heard it before, or know it is not true,
you will stop me; but I do assure of this,
I have learned off by heart from folk who went out from
this self same place who firmly believe it to be true.
Anyway I will get on with it".

So she told her tale.

Was this not the path through the moors that Mysie took on her road home from Edinburgh where she had been in domestic service for the last few months?

We are not the only ones with memories stirring and sad, who looked down from this vantage point, away to the station on the main Carstairs - Edinburgh line. Jamie had loved her from early youth while working together at the screening plant at the nearby colliery, or playing their own private games, and talking their own dreams and plans on the road to another long day's slavery. Worse than that; on a black and bleak morning, shielding her as they walked together before the real world was astir.

He remembered winter mornings when he laid his jacket across her shoulders always making sure that he was on the windward side of her; all the time pretending he was not cold in his thin pit shirt. He remembered the thrill of tying her worn scarf under her small chin and worshipping as he did so. He was glad of his daily morning ritual, although he never did get round to telling her of his love. He was afraid. They were just laddie and lassie.

Would she run away on in front frightened by this adult relationship suggested? Was she just being kind to a wee collier boy? So instead of declaring himself in his own humble way he rather overdid it, by pretending a nonchalance that would have been spurious to an interested person, old and wise enough to tell the truth.

As he stood, he remembered the night of her departure. She had secured a post at the manager's house which had delivered her from the dirt and grime, aye, and the horror she had of the loud clanking machinery, while picking dirt from the coal on the bar conveyor, so that clean coal could be delivered to the

24

wagons. Her hands never got as clean as a girl's of her age should. Neither were they ever clear of the cuts caused by handling the dirt in wet cold conditions of winter. These cuts took ages to heal and never really got a chance.

He never had the same chance to see her after she moved to her new job, for two reasons; her time off was strictly limited, and her place of work was a good distance from the village. Gradually they drifted apart.

Another was not loth to fill the vacuum. There was a teenage son of the house, he was home for the summer vacation at the University. He had time and opportunity on his hand, which he used to promote his pursuit of Mysie. She finally gave in on the old, old assurance that he would take care and nothing would happen. He left soon after to go back to his studies, and left her to manage as best she could. Shortly afterwards she really was on her own, when the lady of the house discovered her condition. Better to get rid of her quickly before her pregnancy was public. One could not have scandal known all abroad; this house and home was above that kind of thing. She was sacked from her post without notice and the mistress was not long in getting her a post in a place in Edinburgh who never asked questions.

Her disgrace; and the humiliation of her new situation, put all aspirations of returning to the village completely out of her mind. Not only so but how could she face the prospect of seeing her boy friend Jamie? He would never want to see her again, although his mother had offered to take her in when she had left her post. At that time neither his mother nor anyone else knew the reason for her leaving.

The final climax came when this new household cast her adrift as well, as she became unfit for the heavy work she had been doing. On the streets of a big city, without a cover for the night and very little money she lay one night in a park in the town. Desperate; she made the resolve; it was either the streets with its starvation and cold, or home to her own village. This was surely the lesser of two evils. She made her way to the station she had left shortly before. As it was winter she waited in the station for a later train. She wanted it to be dark before she got home. She could not face the twitching curtains of the busy bodies' doors. Her return had to be in darkness so that she could creep to a well known door, surely there would be a welcome. She would be safe if she chapped on that door.

Arriving at the station she faced the ordeal of a walk of nearly three miles on a dark and stormy night. She was not afraid of the dark; she was after all, a country lass and she knew the roads through the moors but she was in the last stages of her pregnancy, and she had not been eating properly for weeks. These fears filled her mind a she set off.

She was not long on the road when her little strength began to fail and more and more she had to sit down and rest all the while getting wetter and colder as her thin worn attire did not give the protection that a night like this required. Still she battled on against the increasing ferocity of the north wind, and the gales of water that soaked her to the skin.

Gradually despair added to her anguish. Would she ever reach the village? Where would she find refuge? Doubts were beginning to fill her mind about a sanctuary in Jamie's home. This was her only hope, for her parents had made it quite clear there would be no place for a prodigal daughter, who had shamed them before friend and foe.

In her hallucinations there was only one place seemed feasible. If she could get off this moor alive, she became

26

bouyed up by the feeling, that she would be welcomed in one home. She held on to this, but it looked more doubtful than ever, that she would make it there. She was more often on her knees than on her feet.

She cried out for help but the wind carried the cries of despair away in the direction from which she had come. Nothing but darkness and terror; what if her pains came on her and nobody near? She would lie down and die in her own agony. She had not known much about babies being born. No kind and wise mother had instructed her apart from a regularly mouthed condemnation. If men had the second one there would not be a third. Remorse flooded afresh into her mind; she was to blame entirely for this awful state of affairs. Strangely enough, through all this torment there ran one constant thought. If it had been Jamie on these summer nights all this nightmare would never have happened. He would never have taken advantage of her.

She had lost all sense of time and direction and lay down, convinced that she would not rise again. Again the thought of the warmth of a welcome and a fire to prove it, gave her fresh resolve. She rose even in her exhaustion and shortly she was convinced that there were lights ahead. Surely it could not be far now; with all the rain she would not have seen very far. With the light came renewed hope. This was only a momentary thing. She could hardly crawl; her long heavy shirt and coat had long since lost any semblance of clothing. She was nothing but a bundle of rags, covering a bundle o' bones soaked to the skin and covered in mud.

Still she struggled on. She knew her destination. That home had been her anchor all through her experience of these dreadful months. She knew the occupants and one face in particular she would never forget. What would he say? What would he do? He would not know the scarecrow she was now from the winsome lass he had walked out with on these same fields an eternity ago. That image was gone for all time. These were her last thoughts as she collapsed with a weak cry at the door.

The cry was heard inside in the warmth and quiet of the kitchen, where a husband and wife were sitting at a miner's coal fire. The woman of the house was first away to the door exclaiming as she went "Whae can be at the door on a nicht like this. It's an awfu nicht." With that she opened the door. In the mellow light of the paraffin lamp she espied the bundle on the doorstep. A brief examination proved it was a human being. She shouted into the house. "Come and see this". At her shout her husband was immediately at her side. Between they carried the bundle into the full light of the kitchen.

"Oh its wee Mysie. What in the world has happened to her?" Soon they had her at the fire and proceeded to get her wet filthy clothes off. While doing this the man was told "Run for the doctor, ah think she deed or gey near haun it. Tell him it is life or daith". He obeyed orders. She meantime set about removing the rest of the remaining clothes exclaiming to herself "The bairns expecting; puir wee mite. Whit rotter wid dae this to this lassie?". The girl was quite unconscious of all these efforts although still breathing. She saw the girl was very near her time. No mistake. She was not the village midwife for nothing. Tenderly she worked away at this scrap of humanity so near her time, but as far away from bearing a child as she had ever seen.

She worked feverishly with plenty of hot water from the hob and warm towels, and was able to make her patient comfortable on the rug on the hearth. She would do no more but sat down and patted her hands and rubbed the wan cheeks. "Are they never coming' She fretted. This was her only and continuous complaint "Its gawn tae be too late."

Help was at hand; the door opened and her husband ushered the doctor into the room. He did not recognise the girl, but saw immediately that she was desperately ill. After a brief examination he assisted them to get her into the set in bed. "Plenty of piggy jars and warm blankets in this comfortable room is about all we can do for her, but the bairn she is carrying has not a chance. I've given her something but we will need to watch her all night. She is dehydrated and completely exhausted. Pneumonia will be our biggest fear and she is very near her time. Will I get a neighbour to sit with you?" The woman was quick to respond. "No doctor; the less folk ken aboot this nicht's work the better. Ma man and I will manage. You'll be back before morning."

With that he left assuring them he would be back as soon as he could. He tried hard to get some conveyance to take the patient to hospital, but this was not possible. There would not be time. So the night crept on, when suddenly the man gave a sharp exclamation. "Oh Jamie will be here any meenit. He was doon at the hall. What will we say tae him? He'll be heart broken; He's aye talking about her sometimes blaming himself, some time her, but main often, the rotter that stole her away. He'll be outraged when he sees what kind of state she is in." The ticking of the old wall clock, rudely interrupted by the raucous sounds striking the hour and half hour slowly counted out the time in a timeless night.

It seemed an age before the door opened and the surprised voice of their son called "Whit is wrong? Why are ye no in bed." His mother hushed him and drew him slowly to the bed. Her tears and trembling betrayed her distress and she collapsed with the effort. It took the young man a moment before he recognised who was in his father and mother's bed.

"It's no Mysie mother? It cannae be. Oh mother is she deeing?" "Ah dinnae ken laddie; she is still unconscious but the doctor's been and he says he'll be back before long."

By this time the son had completely lost control of himself, and leaning on the bed he rubbed her poor wasted hands. He was broken hearted and his agony transmitted itself to her. She became restless and appeared to be trying to say something to him. He hushed her and drew her hands close to him but she repulsed him by trying to pull her hands from his grip. Was she really rejecting him? He had tried so hard to put her out of his mind, if not his heart over these last tragic months. Was this her answer to his seeming indifference? How long he stayed anchored by her need, and his love, he never checked. Any way it did not matter; there would be no work for his father and him tomorrow morning aware, that it was now morning.

All this was broken by a knock at the door and the doctor letting himself in with the greeting "It is just the doctor." How glad they were to see his kindly concerned face and rallied to feel that this old friend and family doctor would have some unfailing remedy.

He came to the bed and said to the joy of his audience "She is coming round. I'll carry on with her where I left off." This he did and after some time she opened her eyes briefly before slipping away again. She did not appear to know anything of her surroundings or the company, and despair flooded in once more. The doctor gave them some heart by saying this was quite natural; she would surface again and would gradually recover sufficiently to recognise them, but he added the warning "She is very low and could not predict anything at this point."

Throughout the night he ministered to her needs, as well as enjoining on the mother to get a rest through in the other room. This she reluctantly agreed to, and slipped away after making a fresh pot of tea. He could not move Jamie. Father took a short nap in the big chair. So the night dragged on; but before the blinds were pulled up to let in the winter daylight there was a sound and movement from the bed. Quickly the doctor responded, but it soon became evident that there was little he could do but try and give her a little nourishment. The young man did not need any second bidding when asked to continue his vigil.

At this point there was an interruption; mother roused by the movement and slight commotion appeared in the room. "I thought I heard something. Is the wee lass better"? Soon she too was sitting at the bedside giving sups of refreshing tea to the frail figure in the arms of her son. With this ministration she showed signs of recovery physically, but emotionally she still remained in a terrible state.

From parched lips there came an agitated query." Is that you Jamie"? He had to lean even nearer to catch the whispered words. "What am I doing here? How did I get here"? She was quietened by the intervention of the doctor, that everything was all right, and soon the weary eye lids dropped and she slipped away from them into unconsciousness. James was himself overwrought and hardly heard the kind word of the doctor. "It is perhaps best this way. It might give her time to regain a wee bit strength. Talk quietly to her. She has a far better chance of getting well if she knows that you are here beside her. You love her; that is evident. Is it our bairn she is carrying?" "No it is not; if it had been she would not have been like this. I would have married her. You surely do not think that because we are collier folk in our house that I would put her in the family way. We would have been married before that. I was brought up to know, that, that was the right thing to do."

So the night passed and the day crawled slowly on. No pit; but a vigil far more tiring than a day's darg winning coal, at the new place the manager had asked his father and him to take on that morning. A place of their own - the ultimate success as a collier - getting to the top of the tree, or the top of the heap depending on your perspective.

He relinquished his post at the bed on the insistence of his mother who declared she was rested and he was dead beat. Would he not take a wee walk up the row or even up to the fields beyond after he had a sleep? Exhaustion made him sleep. Had he not been up since yesterday at five o'clock? Add to that a long hard day at the coal face. These factors combined with the agony of these anxious hours made it imperative that he snatch some sleep. He did not need anything from the doctor's bag. The warmth and comfort of the bed his mother had just left, was all that was required to make him fall over with the demand to his father that if there was any change he was to be roused at once.

At that moment the doctor said he would need to go and attend to his morning surgery. He did not leave without drawing the mother aside and telling her to take great care for the girl was not out of the wood yet by a long way. We will have a struggle to keep her with us so don't build up your hopes. So he left to begin another day that had been linked to its predecessor by a waiting watchful night.

Before the day had matured it was evident to Jamie's mother that the girl's frail spirit was failing. How she longed for the doctor to return. She had so much confidence in him. Had she not been with him at many a difficult confinement in her capacity as midwife. If anyone could save the wee lass it would be he, so it was understandable that she should greet him with relief and hope, as he came back after surgery, and a few calls along the rows.

His examination was carefully and considerately done, after which he turned to the family - father had roused from his nap in the big chair and had brought a pailfull of coal into the house from the coalhouse out the back. Jamie had also risen and the trio waited for his verdict. In a few whispered words he

32

drew them away from the bed and gave them his diagnosis. "She has pneumonia, I fear there is little can be done for her. She is weak and under nourished and last night's experience on the moors was the final straw. "Keep her warm and give her some sips of water to wet her lips. She will not take any solids and milk will not help at this stage. I'm very sorry because I feel so helpless. If she only had had some care over the last few weeks it would have been a different story."

Before the doctor left Jamie slipped through the room and gave himself up totally to his grief, and wept his heart out to exhaustion. Finally he gathered himself together, splashed his face with cold water from the zinc pail at the backdoor and crept back to his place beside his lass. He had always thought of her as such during the long months of separation.

He was not long seated when she responded to the clasp of his hand by a fairy touch. Through parched lips she formed the words. "Dinnae leave me Jamie. Haud oan tae ma haun for ah'm fair tired. Oh Jamie ah'm sorry for aa the grief ah hiv caused. What ah did wis wrong, but it would no it if had been you. You ken ah never loved anybody but you. He seemed nice and was kind to me when ah worked at his hoose but ah ken noo it was just a bit o fun he was after. He did nae want to ken me after he went tae the University, and his family goat rid o me. Good riddance to bad rubbish was how his mother put it."

"That's all behind us; we will make up for that when you get better." He whispered with his head close to hers. He could hardly hear her words and certainly could not believe them.

"Darling Ah will no mairy ye. I should hae din so, before ah got into this mess; but not noo. Ah'm dying love. Ah don't need anybody to tell me that. Dinnae brek yir hert for me ah'm no worth it."

Suddenly she was the stronger of the two, as she cradled his head on her breast; the place he had dreamed about during her long absence. The seeming surge of strength was not physical but emotional. She slipped away from him without any struggle. It was over. Was this what death was like? This silence and lack of response; this numbness and helplessness that he felt would never go away.

They buried her with the promise of eternal life in the reading and words of the one taking the service. He barely heard the sermon. Grief and loss were too strong; he wanted her here and now, living and real. It took time for him to appreciate the meaning of the words just uttered. If we have faith there is hope. If that were true he would see her again in heaven. It was all he had on which to rely.

He was back at the pit at their new place. Their task was to win a piece of coal; difficult to work, and adjoining some old waste ground. Their first job was to clean all the rubbish lying around. He brought in some hutches and they worked away till piece time, getting the area cleared ready for getting down to the job; securing the roof and wining coal at the same time. His father was a good miner, one of the best, and careful as well. It was a dangerous place and the old waste did not look good. It had stood abandoned for some time. It was hanging in the air and the timber was well weathered and not very secure. It was during this operation that it happened. The old stoop collapsed with a roar and a crash, burying father and son under tons of debris.

No chance was the verdict, after they were dug out of their temporary burial ground and carried slowly all the way to the pit bottom by men, who like the victims, lived in constant danger of roof falls like this.

34

The doctor was waiting for them as they arrived with their double burden. Word was sent to the surface to get word to the wife and mother. The manager had someone picked for this difficult task. This was one of the worse jobs that could fall to any man because as he moved to the door the occupant immediately senses that something serious has happened, especially if it is in the middle of a shift.

This time was no different. The distraught woman opened the door and before the messenger could utter a word she cried aloud. "Is it my man or is it Jamie." "Its worse. Come into the house." There he told her what he knew of the accident.

Later that morning she stood bereft as men carried their double burden into the house-to a woman-a widow and mother who had just lost a young girl whom she loved with the tenderness that only women know. Yes; a lassie she would have been proud to call her daughter in law. Not only so; a wee life too that in the near future might have called her granny.

So we leave her with her own grief; the victim of so much that was out of her control.

The story affected us both and we were quiet. We felt the chill as the sun for a moment was shaded by a small cloud. Did the recounting of such a tragedy not deserve a salute from the sky?

During this time I wondered what to say. Would it be insensitive to mention similar cases? My reverie was disturbed as she asked if such a thing could be true. I think my reply took her by surprise. "Yes it can be true. I will give you three horrible occasions that I know well. The first concerned a young boy in his teens. His job was to open and shut a ventilation door as every rake of hutches were drawn up the mine. As the full hutches came up towards the door, he opened it to let it through. After it had passed he stepped out on to the track to close it. He followed the correct procedure and was in the act of closing the door when the rope broke and the six full hutches careered back on top of him. Each full hutch carried one ton of coal. I did not know how that message was sent.

Two other instances of this, more modern than the one quoted, will show that it does not become easier. I was well acquainted with both. So I told her of them.

The mine was being driven from one level of coal to another through a down throw fault. The deputy in charge of the mine driving had fired a full round of shots in the face of the drivage, and he with his team of mine drivers had gone well out the road, to give the place time to clean off the fumes from the shots. This was always the procedure. This was the recognised piece time.

It is law that that area has to be examined by the deputy before men are allowed to work in the road after shot firing. He does this, by testing for gas, in and around the face of newly exposed roof and sides; at the same time he examines the road to ensure it is safe for his team to work, with instructions as to the conditions, and how they should be tackled.

On this occasion, the deputy, after he had eaten his piece, went back in, and while carrying out his inspection was caught by a sudden fall of roof. The men rushed inbye, and were able to pull the man clear of the debris. The overman and under-manager were soon on the scene but despite the diligent efforts of the men and officials at the point of the accident, the deputy could not be revived. Word was sent to the surface and then began the onerous task of bearing their neighbour on a stretcher to the pitbottom. This is a very difficult job. In addition to the sudden loss of a man who had been with them through the months of the drivage; who indeed had been with them a few minutes earlier taking their piece, and enjoying the crack (talk). They were faced with the carrying him out of the pit.

The majority of the roads in this pit had a belt conveyor along one side of the road with a track for hutches on the other. This meant that there were places where men could not walk abreast. At great inconvenience two men could walk at the front and two at the back within the rails but it was impossible for anyone to walk along side the stretcher. On this occasion they were one mile from the pitbottom. They had to be spelled at frequent intervals up a long mine with a round and uneven pavement.

It happened on the afternoon shift; as they arrived at the top, the under manager was asked if he would undertake to carry the message to the home. After quickly washing and dressing he went in his car to the village. He stopped some distance along the street and walked back to the house. As he opened the garden gate, and was just a step or two up the path, a woman came rushing down. She had a little child, not yet school age clinging to her apron.

She broke the silence of the summer evening "It's no John; It's no John" and collapsed into his arms.

"Ah ken it wis serious, when ah saw you comin up the path."

He ushered her into the house and started to tell her as best and gently as he could of the accident, that had taken the bread-winner away. She would not be consoled, and it was some time before she would consent to allow a neighbour in to share her grief, while the official went to get a councillor from her church. They were Salvation Army folks, and the man who came was hand picked for the job.

Having fulfilled the task he made his way back to the pit to face up to the investigation that is necessary in an accident as serious as this. By this time the Inspector of Mines was present, as well as high ranking officials at the coal board, so the poor man finished his day by being subjected to a remorseless interrogation of the practice in the case of mine driving.

With this examination ending at two am, and the requirement to be back at the pit by six for the dayshift, sleep was not likely to be on the agenda. The sober fact is this; his widow and her wee lassie would grieve for a husband and father for a long time. For the rest, the tragic event would soon be forgotten in the hurley burley of coal getting in the pit, and even in the mine where it all happened.

Another case involved the same man. This time a large fall had taken place on a five hundred feet faceline on the nighshift. This meant that no coal could be produced on dayshift. He went underground to determine the full extent of the damage. After that he picked the men for the job and set them in two teams - one on either side of the fall. They were specialists in this type of work. It had happened quite near the main road some hundred feet away. So a team was despatched to the topside; this necessitated walking from the main gate right round and in the tail gate, and finally down the faceline for four hundred feet over cut coal with their tools.

The undermanager spent most of his day with the men, apart from a brief visit to ascertain how the rest of the pit was doing.

Towards the end of the sift he was up at the topside checking what progress had been made, and assessing the work for the afternoon shift. It was understood by all miners in a situation like this, that you did not crawl over a fall where there were no supports. You take the long way round.

Unknown to him an official had gone over at the beginning of the shift. This fact had been noted by the men; so when the undermanager had left, an altercation took place between the men, as to the feasibility of going over the top. No official would know and one of the miners played his trump card. I'm not going the long way. The official went over the top this morning. If he can do it so can I."

The undermanager had only left a few minutes, and was nearing the top road when there was a shout "Jimmy has been caught in a fall." As he hurried back he was told of the argument and Jimmy's decision to crawl over the top where there was the large cavity, left by the fallen roof.

At this point the official is in a no win situation. A man is buried beneath fallen rock with an unsupported roof above. Miners at this point invariably take the line; one of our mates is in there, but we'll get him out. At this point it is unknown if the man is dead or alive. It is easy to understand the men's anxiety and the eagerness to get their workmate out, and they will take terrible risks. The official has to step in and inforce the law. You support the place before you attempt to rescue the man. There is no use in perhaps saving the one man if you lose three or four in the attempt. There always will be men who will take the opposite view, and harp on about it long afterwards.

There was a sequel to this incident. When a fatality occurs the officials at the pit get in touch with the man's priest or minister; he is deemed to be the best agent for this difficult task. On this occasion the secretary phoned the man's church and they agreed to convey the message.

As is usual the manager's office was busy all afternoon and well into the evening, when suddenly two men burst into the office looking for the manager. They were intent in doing him some damage and had to be forcibly restrained. Their grievance, and it was a legitimate one, was this. "Our mother heard about my father's death from a neighbour when she was at the Co for her messages, well after the accident." The message had not been delivered.

Grief can so easily turn to rage in a situation like that.

When something like this happens and is reported to the official, if he is not actually on the scene; perhaps his first reaction is to say. "Am I to blame? Was there a sufficient supply of timber; were the props set at the correct distance?" Is the thought of self preservation the keynote in such a situation as this if in some way you were to blame then the thing would be very difficult to live with, unless you were very uncaring and hard. It might take a long time to recover from the trauma; after the others had forgotten all about it.

CHAPTER 2

MIGRATION - HAYWOOD

Dealing still with the 1891 records. Movement from England was confined to one person. John Muir of Durham was the only one, while Wales lost one its sons to the village. Ireland made up the deficit.Fifty eight-forty one males and seventeen women.

These are listed below.

In Schedule 1-82.

Total born in the Parish of Carnwath = 185.
Total born outside the Parish = 260
Of this total 21 men and seven women were born in Ireland.

In Schedule 83-163

Total born in Parish of Carnwath=127

Total born outwith Parish of Carnwath=259 giving a total of 386.

Of this total seventeen men and ten women were born in Ireland.

In Schedule 163-224.

Total born in Parish of Carnwath=140 = 46%.

Total born outwith the Parish of Carnwath 120 giving a total of 260 = 54%

On top of this total were three men born in Ireland.

The census shows in 1891 total population of 1091.

Only in the last of the schedules were more people born in the Parish than outside. This would make it a cosmopolitan group. The thing of interest at this point, that must be considered, is this. It was a new mining area and the population, to fulfil the needs of this new venture would be gathered from adjacent pits, whose life had finished. Young men and women would move more easily than older ones, to pastures new.

Added to this movement, it is obvious from the figures shown, there was a shift from a wider area. So while the central belt would supply the larger percent, the net was cast further than that.

Word would be carried that there was work in this faraway place, and young folk, although they were not of mining heritage took up the challenge. This might be called the positive side of this migration. In their own towns and villages conditions were hard; this caused a regular drain of the fittest. The 'Clearances' with other harsh treatment drove the bravest and most venturesome on boats to the farthest corner of the globe at least to the parts coloured Red-The British Empire..

Proportionally Scotland sent more emigrants to build the empire than the rest of these islands. But large numbers did not move so far afield; they filled the great conurbation's of the industrial belt.

Worldwide movement of population had been spasmodic as well as sparse for centuries, but this situation changed rapidly over the last three hundred years, with the advent, easier means of travel. The discovery of the new world was the catalyst. Men and women were ripe for change - bad conditions of employment, allied to poor wages, made this well nigh imperative.

Scotland must rank among the top of the bill. The discovery of coal and its subsequent mining brought about the drift from rural places to towns and villages where this was carried on. We talk of Scotland particularly.

It had essentially been the home of large heards of cattle. Along with this, there were fertile areas where crops, especially oats, flax with root crops, provided for man as well as animals. Sheep were herded in wide wild tracts of mountain and dale in large numbers. This did not sustain a large population.

Heron 1791-Scotland Delineated - makes some interesting observations. The country is drained of its inhabitants, by the emigration of individuals tempted by the illusive view of riches. However, the improvements the industry and riches, lately intro-duced into Scotland form a striking contrast with the barbarity, indolence and the poverty of former times. This favourable change may be considered as the effect of those enlightened views, and those liberal principles, for which many spirited friends of Scotland, are at this time so eminently distinguished.

Luxury is generally the concomitant of opulence. In dress and habit the Scots have begun to emulate their more wealthy neighbours. It is a well known fact that some ordinary mechanics are now better clothed and fed and better lodged, than many of the most eminent persons in the nation were, not a hundred years ago.

Natural prejudices are gradually losing ground on both sides; the dress and the manners of the English, begin to gain the ascendancy. In short the happy era seems not very distant, when the English and Scots shall be, in every sense of the word - One Nation.

Pertinent to our present study is the statement; The riches, beauty, and variety of this area (Haywood is included,) entitle it to a particular notice in a Delineation of Scotland. Of all its fossils and mineral productions, coal is the most valuable.

The industry of its inhabitants is deservedly repaid by their success in the manufacturing line. Their number may amount to about one hundred and twenty five thousand.

During this period the whole of the continent of Europe was experiencing great movements of population but the fact was this, that Scotland suffered a greater loss proportionally than most countries...Relative to the rest of Britain the rate of emigration was much higher than England and Wales. So the position arises, that not only is there a large movement from the rural districts to the urban, but this is seen in figures for overseas.

In the home market the magnet was larger wages and shorter hours. This was the case within Scottish borders, but wages for comparable work higher in England, so there would be a natural drift south of the border. In reality statistics from 1851, 1891 of inward movement tell us that two men came to the village in the earlier census - one from England and one from Wales; while the latter shows one only from England. This was offset in great measure by a considerable influx from Ireland.

This in turn brought its own problems. Presbyterianism in Scotland was strong, but the balance was upset by this so it became a two way thing. Many Scots left these shores to settle in Northern Ireland; there too, this has led to problems.

Nevertheless we must not get the impression that this movement was the sole prerogative of the poorer classes. Many people with learning and skills in trade and industry looked beyond these shores, so the land was drained of this valuable asset, while the land of the north and the south, gave its fair measure to populate the industrial areas. In this connection mention must be made of the 'Highland Clearances'. Many moved but this was only a temporary measure, for emigration was quite widespread. Scotland was to give of its entrepreneurial skills to every corner of the globe. There was definitely a 'Brain Drain', and Scotland must have been the poorer.

There were few families in the district of Forth. Wilsontown and Haywood who had not seen friends and relatives move further afield. At home wages were poor during the long period of the nineteenth century and well into the twenty. In mining, glaring examples are not isolated. Large land owners were being subsidised more per ton brought up the pit than men who produced it. One example; £100,000 in royalties in one year.

The declaration of war in 1914 was to bring the miners' response. As of an earlier age - Clearances - many flocked to the colours. It is estimated that 25% responded to the call. Again as in the Clearances they were considered among the best of soldiers. If conditions were bad before the war, they did not improve afterwards, and the men who had answered the urgent call to fight, came home to a future that was no future..

During this time people were not the only export. Heavy industries that had been the backbone of our livelihood weregradually and systematically moved to England. That story is still incomplete.

CHAPTER 3

MINING IN SCOTLAND

Coal was mined in Scotland for over 750 years. The earliest in the country and probably in the world ever noted was the contemporary copy of a charter dated as early as 1219 . It was granted to Newbattle Abbey for the Earl of Winchester "Seye de Quinci. It was copied into the Abbey cartulary, he register of charters. It was lost to France in the middle of the 17t C, and only came back to Scotland about 1720, when it was purchased by the Faculty of Advocates, whose books later became the National Library.

Religious orders were early associated with coal mining as far as any references are known. Monks at Dunfermline Abbey were given the right to take coal at Pittencrieff in 1291, followed by Paisley Abbey. It has always been assumed that production was by the monks. This may have been true very early on and on a very small scale.

Colliers living in the vicinity of the monastery walls dug the coal, and gradually little communities of miners and their families were formed. In 1430 it is recorded of poor begging at church doors, and departing with joy on their faces on receiving stones as alms, which burned, instead of wood, of which the country is distitute-Aeneas Syleous, who later became Pope Pious II related in DE Europa accounts of his travels.

The use of coal was confined to the narrows of the Lowlands; one early working was near Bo'ness. It was not till the beginning of the 16C, that coal was used for domestic purposes, except around the Forth estuary. Reports of coal being exported to Ireland; in 1545 Tynes Morrison reported this. By this time coal was being worked in Fyfe which was 'richt profitable for operations of smiths'. The commercial value of coal was being recognised, so coal output in the middle of the 16C had increased twelve fold and primitive working was commenced. In 1575 the Abbot of Culnoss granted the lease of coal workings to Sir George a man renowned for his mechanical knowledge. This was a wise choice and he sunk a pit on the shore and one on a small island offshore. This meant double egress, the shafts being connected under the Forth. A moat surrounded to prevent flooding. Two means of egress were not made compulsory till well on in the 19C. This was made after men were entombed in a single shaft.

An excerpt from the Scotsman dated Monday 31st July 1985 reveals that coal mining was not the only industry that had a disgraceful record.

Quoting Pic Botha- mining minister...

"Each tonne of gold produced in S.Africa costs an average of more or less one human life and twelve seriously injured miners. This is exceptionally high by any standards, and inter-nationally we compare badly." He said this to a congress of the Southern African Miners' Federation.

"The group claims a membership of 1.5 million workers across the region. Last year 485 people were killed in S.A mine accidents, and more than 69,000 miners have died in the countries mines since 1911.

This May 104 men died when an underground train plunged down a shaft at Vaal Reef's goldmine, south west of Johannesburg, crushing the lift carrying men to their work. The mine federation president James Motatsi, told congress that on average one man was killed in S.A's mines every day.

"The only conclusion I can come to is this; black mineworkers are subsidising mining production with their lives. There is no technical reason why mining should not be absolutely safe. The only obstacle is finance. We must insist that this butchery stop, or the production."

Mr Botha said S.A had made progress after a judicial commission of inquiry into safety and health in mines - the first for 30 years. The inquiry recommended that the government, employers and workers set up a committee to draft new laws for the industry. That approach held the promise of stabilising a minerals policy acceptable to all.

The output from S.A goldmines which dominate the industry fell 35 tonnes last year to 584 tonnes - the lowest level since 1958-Reuter.

Quoting Rex Merrifield Broederstroom

It would appear that Scotlands mines have not held the monopoly of dreadful conditions and accidents.

Going back to the beginning of mines in Scotland; in 1618 a pit in Culross described by Taylor the Poet. They did dig deep 40 feet right into a rock. At last they found seacoal. When men are at work below, one hundred ships may pass over their heads. The mine was cut like an arch or vault. A man may walk upright in most places."

The first machine to raise water from a pit, was operating before 1600. It was still an innovation, when one was installed in the Moat pit, as the Culross was called. The machine was a water gin-a serious of wooden buckets attached to an endless chain passing over the top of an axle on the surface. Coal was sometimes raised by this means.

The coal works in Culross were the greatest in Scotland but a storm in 1625 damaged the machinery and the moat built on the island, as a safeguard for the pits long since breached. Culross finally closed in 1789 and the colliers moved on. In the statistical Account of Scotland compiled a few years later we read. "However certain rich seams remain especially at Valleyfield.(it closed in 1981) At the beginning of the 17C. It has been estimated that 50 pits were working with some producing 15000 in a year. In 1636 coal was sold at 3/- a chaldron (perhaps 30 cwt.) with carriage at 2/8."

Things should be noted at this point; in the 1930's coal was put in the wagon at 2/6 per ton with all overheads cleared at Kingshill No 2. Men at that time were paid 8/9d on cost and 9/6d on face work per shift. This pit was producing about 1000 tons on the dayshift. A hutch was reckoned to hold one ton of coal. If 1000 hutches were wound to the surface in a shift the manager agreed with the men working in and around the pit bottom that each would get the price of a new bonnet-2/6d. That was a great incentive indeed. I know. I was there as a participant.

Reverting to our original text;

In 1870 coal fetched 5/-a ton, but in 1875 it was making 16/-to 18/-. Mens' wages rose to the unheard of rate of 10/- per shift for a 10 hour day although in Fife they were already on 8 hours shift.

1872 was the first year in which the mine owners had to make official returns of persons employed and tonnage raised. In the first return the Eastern District of Scotland 144 boys between 10 and 12 years were employed. From this time output increased dramatically. Production in 1873 was 16.5 million tons with manpower at 74,000 equal to 227.02T/man/shift per year equal to.725 tons per man shift.

By 1893 production rose to 25.4 million tons with 90,000 men; that makes 288.2 tons/man/years so production was .9 tons. During this period the size of coal companies rose sharply. In 1873 one company produced 500,000 tons per year and between 400,000 and 500,000 tons per year.

From being individual units in a local setting, but with deeper sinkings, the trend changed, and the time of the public companies with larger outputs arrived. The money came easily as the trade was so prosperous. One interesting name comes into the debate. Lord Alfred Spencer Churchill formed the Fifeshire Main Collieries Company in 1890, (was a descendent of his prepared to take on the miners of South Wales in 1926?) Maybe the hard work of these same men helped to create the wealth of the line.

Two things came out of this; the encroaching nature of the monopoly from England on rich pickings in Scotland. The other is simple; labour was cheap and miners' lives expendable. It was during this time that the best and most easily worked as well as the less expensive was 'Herried'. The Scots word has it right. To a country person the word is aptly fitting. To herrie a nest is to rob it of the eggs or young, or a beehive of its honey. In the incident above it means to rob or plunder.

In 1878 output was 18 million tons. From then till 1913 1000 million tons were raised with 58% coming from the central belt. 1913 was the peak year 42,456,516 with 147,000 miners. There were 475 pits operated but 180 companies. Output/man year for underground workers was 385 tons against the figure for Britain 325 tons. The Scottish coalfield had the highest man year of any field. Output per shift was 1 ton.

The proportion of total manpower was 12% while proportion of output was 14% in Scotland.95% was won by hand. The minimum wage was 7/2 (36p) i.e the average per shift Face workers received 50/(2.50) Oncost and surface earned 33/-(1.65.) and 28/- (1.40) per shift week.

In Lanarkshire with which we are mainly concerned, dozens of high production pits worked at one point or another in every square mile of the Clyde Valley. Pit bings practically encroached on one another. Many of these pits went for 100 years, before they closed. Around 1913 thirty of the pits in Lanarkshire employed 700 - 1000 ; many employed only 200.

The great war, plus the crippling strikes of 1921 and 1926 had a disastrous effect and there was a decline in output of 10 million tons between 1923-1939, from 23 to 13 million. This decline was mainly in Lanarkshire where the bigger seams were being exhausted.

The earliest reference to coal in Lanarkshire is in Carluke in 1650. By 1900 250 collieries were working. By 1834 at Carnwath coal had been worked for many years. The Wilson brothers had begun an iron foundry in 1779, but the good coal lay deep with much water, and they were forced to work a poorer quality until 1788; a steam engine allowed them back into the better coal. By 1807, 2000 were employed or dependent on the iron works, but it closed in 1812 and was not reopened till 1821 when it was bought by Dixons. Dealt with in the chapter on Wilsontown. This was a period of great prosperity. By 1862 there were 120 blast furnaces at work in Scotland, and nearly half the iron manufactured came from the district of Coatbridge and the county of Lanark. This prosperity did not percolate down through the strata of society to the bottom layer; the men and women at the bottom of the pile. This debunks a theory resurrected in the late years of the 20C Market Forces were to be the salvation of the nation. If the top layer make money the spin off will bring similar blessings to all. It was not true then and it is not true now. Humanity has not evolved in this fashion.

Accompanying this gathering of wealth there was a parallel upsurge in discontent about wages and conditions of work and the accidents and inquiries increased. In 1851 saw conditions so bad that wages were as low as 2/-per day in the shire's expanding industry. In 1852 mines in Lanarkshire asked for an extra shilling per day as this was inadequate to keep them in the state to which they were entitled."

In March 1856 employers cut wages by 20%, and a month later 30,000 men were idle. Up until 1859 women were still employed underground in the Lothians. By 1900 output was 17,174,247 tons. It should be noted at this point that as early as 1606 the Scots Parliament passed an infamous law binding the colliers to their pits. So they could not go to other pits or other work. It was a life sentence.

About 1592 a fire at Faside pit forced the passing of an act condemning miners to a life of slavery for nearly 200 years. They were freed from this type of slavery in 1799. One authority at the time said "Considering the high rate of wages, and the many prerequisites they do not deserve half their wages."

Wages ranged from 17/-22/6 for men   )

      "   "   5/-7/- for women) per week
      "   "   2/-5/- for children)

Bald was to say-women who carried from the face to the bottom of the shaft, and up ladders, to the surface equalled carrying a cwt of coal to the top of Ben Lomond. A girl of twelve was making 40-50 trips a day carrying 2 cwt. A regular load for a bearer in the Edge Seams was 12-14 stones, and on the flat 16-20 stones. A commission was set up around this time and at Redding Collery was told by 11 years George Murdoch. "I go down the pit at 2 in the morning, sometimes 3 and return at 5 the next day." Janet Cumming 11 years, a bearer "I gang at 5, and come up at 5 at night. Work all night Friday and come away at 12 in the day on Saturday."

These are only a few examples found in the records of the Commissioners. There are many more cases of slavery throughout Scotland. It is on record that the manager of Sir Wm Baillie's mines at Polkement said. "We have no record of accidents; nor is it customary to keep such, not even of accidental sudden deaths."

The manager of a number of pits, owned by a wealthy landowner said; "I see no particular advantage would be derived from excluding women from the pits as they are used to the work, and are fit for nothing else. It might increase the price of coal by 2d in the ton."

During this long period in the evolution of coal mining, parallel to the hardships and atrocious conditions in the mines, there grew up pockets of resistance all over the country by groups of men determined to fight for better conditions. These associations or unions as they eventually became known, bravely stuck to their tasks, there were many setbacks in this battle. Strikes were frequent and widespread but very spasmodic, owing to the fact that pits were isolated from each other their own little village grown up around the pit. The village of which we deal with here is a prime example of this- more than twenty rows of miners' houses of single ends or two rooms owned by the company. This was indeed a continuation of the tied house system evidenced in rural areas where farmers and landowners used this to their own advantage. A man was more likely to toe the line, if, in addition to losing his job, he would also lose his house as well.

Notwithstanding, some were prepared to fight this bonded slavery, and strikes were frequent. Of special importance some must have a mention. Wage cuts in 1874, after the price of coal had reached the high level of 1873 were of 10% 20% even 30% . Strikes were frequent, but in isolated areas, and did not produce any improvement and finally collapsed. Wages were cut by 50% of what they had been nine months earlier.

This had a serious effect; many disillusioned miners left the association of workers (Miners's National Union) but by 1876 in Fife and Clackmanan, proposed wage cuts led to a threat of strike action. Miners finally agreed to reductions down to a minimum. This was an organised retreat. In Lanarkshire at the same time May 1876 wages had been driven down to 3s in some pits so that the darg which two years previously had brought in 11s 4p now brought in 3s 4p.

In 1877 the country had a financial crisis; it was proposed to have a reduction in wages. Confrontation now became the order of the day. This was brought to a head in March of that year. The colliers in Clakmanan found posters posted up in all works intimating that miners' wages were to be reduced by 10%, and in future they were to be charged for house, rent and coal. On May 19th the owners decided on a lockout to enforce the reduction. By May 26th 4000 men were out of work, 700

54

struck work while the rest were locked out. It lasted fourteen weeks ending in a substantial victory for the men. It was the first big dispute between a well organised county union and the federation of employers. This may be regarded as a landmark in the history of the Scottish miners.

A strike in Ayrshire 1881-1882 for wages failed. The turbulent times continued with unions having very up and down times. Wages in Britain were very low but worse in Scotland. In 1894; the first time a ballot was held in the Scottish coalfield., not in a single collieryor in a district, and the vote decreed that there should be a call for strike by all miners in Scotland. There was a ratio of two members to one union, but there was a solidarity that had been lacking. This after fifty years was an indication of the depth of feeling, and was strong enough to set out on a course of action, the onlooker would have deemed impossible. Much disarray and disagreement among leaders whether they should accept 6s reduction instead of 1/- per day did not help the cause.

By the end of September, after eleven weeks of strike the authorities made use of the Police to break up miners' strike meetings. Many and lurid are the details of this high handed action. In all 70,000 men were on strike.

By the end of October 1894 the strike was finished: wages had gone down in Lanarkshire by 20% from the 1888 basic of 4/- a day to 3/-. While in the Lothians by 20% down to 3/2d.

This wretched situation caused dismay and disarray and many left the union. (Figures quoted tell this) In 1894 the figure was 35,000; in 1859 20,920; 1896 17,950; and 157,000 in 1897.

Ferment and disillusionment erupted over the next few years over a minimum wage. When this was rejected in

December 20th 1911 there was no further discussion. In January 1912 there was a ballot held in which there was a four to one majority for strike action to enforce the claim for a minimum wage. Scottish share of the ballot was five to one. In Scotland a minimum wage of 6s/day would be acceptable; In Yorkshire and Nottingham 7/6d.

The government intervened and a four point plan was laid out, mainly in favour of the owners. This statement was issued on February 27th. On March 1st no seams in Britain were working. This caused widespread chaos; other industries were soon affected; trains and shipping were at a standstill. Since coal was the main source of heat and energy, households felt the want as well.

Was it about this time that a famous quotation was born. "Like old Asquith we'll just wait and see." It was a favourite saying of my mothers in our home. Throughout the month of March 1912 there were demands for action by the government, but Asquith and his compatriots decided to wait and see.

During all this time the miners had a bad press. No one seemed to support them, although there was one man, Tom Mann printer and publisher who was arrested for a leaflet in the Syndicalist "Don't Shoot."

During all this time numbers increased in employment until 1913 the greatest number of men were employed and, out-put was the highest ever recorded; 287 million tons were raised in British mines. The next major crisis in the industry came in 1921 when a strike lasted for three months. Police and soldiers were quickly called out to prevent colliers gathering in numbers to prevent safety men, pumper and boiler firemen attending their work. A troubled period followed and in reality was only a continuation of the battle against bad conditions and

56

low wages. Except in the years of the first world war, when a greater enemy was being fought and harder battles being lost and won, things reverted to the age long strike about low wages and bad conditions.

The government and the coal owners spent the time from July 1925 in preparation for a showdown in the spring of 1926, so May 4th saw the start of the national strike, when the country was paralysed, the strike lasted for 9 days. The miners carried on the strike for 7 months.

The writer has some recollection of these days although he was quite young. One of the great problems in the strike period was the dissension among the leaders of the miners. It had come down to the level of mere survival; relief was beginning to dry up and the government was playing its cards well, bringing pressure to bear on the unions.

They were reduced to the soup kitchens; a plate of soup and a hunk of bread, was quite the staple diet in many homes. One feature that must be noted, was the disagreement about prolonging the strike, or for survival's sake, taking the reduced offer, and going back to work worse off than they were before the stoppage.

Communities were divided. Rows of houses had their fair share of strife. Families were split as well. Farmers' fields were raided for turnips and potatoes; the staple food. Starvation was not something that belonged to an earlier age, or some backwood country; but an important part of the British Empire.

Men went back to work with a grudge, and recrimina-tions were rife among workmates; some wanting to go back for lower wages, but a crust was better than no bread at all. This meant that on return to work, relationship was strained and difficult, and the word 'Blackleg' was bantered back and forth regularly.

An example of this; a man on oncost work who never attended a union meeting at the pit always made himself available for work when the meeting agreed to have an idle day. He did not seem to be greatly concerned, when other men refused to have anything to do with him. He was self sufficient enough to be content with his work and conditions, that enabled him to care for his family, although there were weighted hints and innuendoes thrown at his wife and family.

CHAPTER 4

MINING IN LATER DAYS

This has been the history of mining communities as emphasised in all discovery of coal. A hole in the ground with, coal as the result of the effort, for the owners. There were other scores chalked up in this contest; good coal for miners' fires in hovels at cheap rates, and coppers to pay the Co. Book, in the purchase of moleskin trousers, salmon pink drawers and pit boots; so you kept on the treadmill. You could not stop. If you did you fell to the bottom of the pile. These were the good old days of hard work or penury, hounded by the need as husband and father to provide for wife and weans: to put up with any conditions and situations, because there were unemployed men at the pithead looking for work when you came up the pit. So the choice was stark and basic. You put up with things as they were.

A favourite statement around then. "Aye there's plenty of work but there is nae money in it." One wag was heard to say; "ah could get washing the dishes for the wife for nothing." Ears listen and young minds develop, and from these judgments are formed as well.

This is not a diatribe against a system of iniquitous exploitation but the judgment of circumstances as they affected the warp and woof of ordinary people's lives. They had no illusions of grandeur or pretensions to any higher order of life.

That was your place and you kept it with a determined effort and struggle. The coal owners created the framework, and circumstances dictated the end result.

There were other ends to this state of affairs; it began in most men a deep burning anger and a resentment that embittered lives and left them hopeless and helpless - no future but the next shift, or worse still, the fear of idle time or accident. So the quality slipped inexorably down, more and more to animal level, until they assumed that mantle. Apathy could also be the offspring; so were set up fertile conditions for seeds of bitterness between miners themselves and this over flowed to the miners' rows. Relationships could become strained and neighbours would be divided; even wives and husbands experienced strife. This angst was real, strong and far reaching; some were not prepared to put up with this and militancy took up the fight on occasions and men were sometimes black listed from one pit, and found the other owners would not take them on at other collieries.

The strikes of 1921 and 1926 were to have profound effects, accruing from years of subjugation and near slavery. Much has been written of the part played by the miner's unions, but it must be granted that every thing gained for miners was won by dedicated men who saw further than the next shift on the next day. They were committed, in their consternation and concern, wit and determination, to channel the hurt and aggrievement into fighting for living conditions for men and their families. Another statement readily banded about; "a breeding ground for Communism." As bourne out in fact in many areas. There seemed to be no common ground but only the inevitable confrontation of suspicion and hatred.

Early life under the hierarchy of coal companies was deeply affected. What shall be said of men who took the workman's train

60

before six a.m.; worked all day at the stint of coal, and failing to get their stint cleaned up and coal filled, because of delays to the haulage system etc, were not allowed to leave until their darg was complete? Yes, the lousing time was 2-25pm, but many times without, the men having answered the call to help with some maintenance task would be late in getting to the pit head. The train for Heywood left Wilsontown at 3-55pm. So they would catch the next one around 6pm. So the day was past; it was home for the bine (dinner and supper in the one dish). You were not likely to go out and have a game of football. It was bed, in preparation for the workman's train in the morning, and the outlook of getting rid of between sixteen and eighteen tons of coal with pick shovel and hammer. Of course if you missed that train you could get home with the one at 8 pm. Overtime was never paid for.

These were the days at the beginning of conveyors and longwall working; this was a development from the stoop and room idea, and the days of hand drawing. This latter was one of the most sustained acts of slavery you could imagine.

They were called drawers, not of water as mentioned in the Bible, but of hutches filled with coal. The job was to fill the hutches as the faceman won the coal, and threw it out on to the roadway.

To keep the story in perspective it must be noted that for economy reasons these roads would be of minimum dimensions; room for a hutch was the criteria. The hutch held about eight cwt, so it did not take a big area; the drawer had to fit into this, and many were the scars on his back and arms trying to push tubs in and out of a road four to five fee high and the same in width. A drawer was noted for the knots on his spinal column damaged by low wooden bars set to support the roof or simply by the low roof itself, if no bars were set. The places worked were not always level, and where the gradient was against the full tub it could be hard work indeed, to bring it out to the bye where it was coupled with tubs from other roads, and taken outbye, either with ponies or latterly by rope haulage.

At times the gradient was so severe that the drawer would need assistance. This was a matter of great debate. In a cross section of men there are differences in strengths, so if there were twelve to twenty drawers the degree of ability varied quite substantially. Over against that there was the more personal quality of willingness to go to the limit before asking for help.

The putter, as this extra man was called, was invariably a further burden on the other men; this man's wages had to be paid, and often this was, at least, in part, paid out of the earnings for the road. If father and son worked the place together then a home would be affected.

Conditions could vary considerably from road to road, so coal could be won more easily in one place than another. All these things led to bickering and ill will among the men. Internationally men cannot agree, and in nations and regions peace is forfeit. So it was in the pit, and this state of affairs suited the owners.

Setting man against man is the oldest trick in the book; the ploy always worked, scant attention being paid to complaints about bad conditions; The reason for complaints were numerous, bad roof, pavement and roof water, air that was not fit for men to work in. The variation of conditions was legion.

There was the age old answer to any grievance; if you did not like it, you were told what to do, and it could be soul destroying to come up the pit at finishing time and find a crowd of men looking for a job. Men as desperate as you were for work, as you, were determined to hold your job. This was inclined to influence your attitude to your problem; so instead of going the last mile in the stand against oppression and fearfully injustice, vocally to other workmen and all who would listen - making sure you were out of hearing of those you were cursing, at home you had a captive audience; you nagged the wife, kicked the cat and cuffed the weans, and so to bed. You need your bed.

These individual jobs were superseded by the Contracting System. This proved that the source of hardship was not confined to one strata of society. The use of men allowed this to gravitate through the pit. One example of this, and if proof were needed for the previous comments, this could be it.

Take a section 600 feet long with a roadway driven in the centre, and a tailgate at each end. These roads served a dual purpose; a means for taking air through the faceline as well as a way for men to get to their work. THESE ROADS WERE ESSENTIAL FOR THE SUPPLY OF MATERIAL. The main road or gate was the largest of these being used for the conveyance of coal outbye. There were five small roads between the bigger ones. Each of the small roads had a man each; the main road employed five. The tail roads had three each. The big road was supported with 12 by 10 feet girders and the system worked after this fashion. The faceline had a chain conveyor on one side and a belt on the other. Coal was won off the face on the dayshift, and advanced the face four and a half feet every shift while the roads were advanced on the nightshift thus keeping up with the faceline. It is with these roads that we are concerned now.

At that time miners worked six days every week. The contractor agreed a price with the management for a set figure for each road with the knowledge it would advance at the same rate as the face. It did not work quite like that. When the brushers (THE NAME FOR THE MEN WHO WORKED ON THE ROAD) came out on the nightshift on Sunday they were faced with four and a half feet of rock to take off the roadway lying back from the face. Now keep in mind that the colliers on dayshift had worked six shifts to advance the face this total distance, it might be assumed that the brushers would work at their normal task that night. It did not work that way, the road was put off that night, and the men put on to another task. This could mean making a refuge hole on the haulage road, or some other work. The making of these manholes was on a separate contract so literally the only man who gained from this was the contractor. This meant that the team took off six days cutting on five shifts. Who do you think was the winner in this unfair contest?. This was made worse when the contractor was in the big road team.

He was the fifth man on the road; the first job of the team was to prepare the road by setting breakers to prevent the explosive from blowing material beyond the extent of the road so preventing unsafe conditions on the faceline. These were wooden props. One man was employed on this; the other four men drilled the holes and cleaned out the pack seats - where the dirt was packed from the debris blown down.

The volume on one side to be packed with loose material from the blown mateial was 12ft long, 3.5 ft high and 4 ft wide. The only difference on the other side was the length 18ft. The total volume would be about 472c ft - 288.5 cft the large side and 189 cft on the other. Depending on the type of rock its weight might be between 16 and 18 tons. One man on each side shovelled to the other man, so it was a case of two men shovelling not five, from the pile. Finally a steel arched girder had to be set for safety purposes. Three men were employed on one side of the road and two on the other. The loose material was packed in tightly to support the roof and

64

the road.   It was not thrown haphazardly, but had to be contained within a strongly built dyke. No dirt was allowed to be filled away on the loader.

Now to give a resume of the fifth man; the contractor; while the preparation was going on, he would go round the section checking up on all the other workmen in his contract. This normally took till after the shots were fired, and he would appear back as the team were eating their piece. He would sit down and have his in peace as the men started to pack away the heavy dirt.   When he was finished he put the stilts on the girder; this allowed the road to settle 12 inches before the road took the weight.

The philosophy behind this was complex. Coal had to be won at the cheapest possible rate, so at the top of the management and owners priorities, was a system adapted for this purpose. What better way than to give the power of payment and work rate, into the hands of a few chosen men, who worked with, and lived in the same row of houses, or in more modern times council houses.   These were men who could do all the work that was asked of them, and were confident of their ability. This; combined with a great deal of avarice and no small helping of cunning (flyness would be the colloquial term) made them ideal for this.

The task of all leaders was made easier by the lack of confidence in the miners, of their own ability and their fear of failure, if they had to make their own personal decisions, and work them out at the coal face. The unions took a long time to address this problem but the owners knew the truth and benefit of raising servants to managers standards, without their being aware they too were being exploited.   Added to this was the acceptance of the wrongly conceived idea that this was their station in life, and there they had to bide.

People like my parents were not immune from this, because they went to the gospel hall. In fact I came to realise, that invariable they would accept and suffer, because they did not want to be classed as trouble makers. Their hope was not that men would better things, either men or masters. Humanity in itself could not lift away from this position. Their hope was that Jesus Christ alone could change things; had he not promised to do so if faith was exercised in him. There never would be a utopia till he reigned; in individuals as well as nations. Their faith was based on the historical fact of Jesus Christ crucified buried and risen from the grave and gone back to heaven. It gave a special feeling of hope in the midst of hopelessness; maybe per chance a clock of martyrdom. THEY LIVED THEIR LIVES in the light of another world where all injustice and suppression would be gone forever. This led to the conception that Christianity was a negative thing, and consisted of rules and regulations.

One outstanding example to balance things; Tom Clarke; who did not warrant widespread notice, but who gave his life for the men in Climpy and Kingshill pits. At the end of the day when he was blacklisted from the pit, no one stood with him, and he went idle for a long time.

On a personal observation; the writer was employed in the pit bottom area, and this meant that I did not need to go down till the last of the men-the last tow we termed it. Tom always went down on this, for he was much in demand by the miners to discuss problems and try and sort things out. One morning the undermanager said to me., "The manager wants to see you in his office when you come up the pit." YOU DID NOT DISOBEY although you knew you were in for a row. The undermanager had spoken to me on a few occasions that I should not keep company with this old Red Flag singer. The sequel to this was interesting; when I failed to give the

66

assurance I would do as instructed, I was told to start on Sunday nightshift on the brushing; so was accomplished what had been a sore point for weeks and a regular complaint, leaving both parties happy. This friendship lasted for years, till the old man died and was buried in Wilsontown Churchyard - it was a strange friendship. Apart from an affinity as work men, their ideals were poles apart. Many were the arguments between them; none were malicious, and the bond between this old communist and the young Christian was real. He was a rough diamond, but it gleamed the brighter the nearer you came to him.

What shall be said of the wives' part in the distribution of the wealth of the weekly wage.

If the men were downtrodden, how did the wives feel? The men could escape to the oblivion of the sawdust for a few hours on paynight and if money stretched, to a Saturday, while the wives stayed at home with the weans. Did they dread bedtime when the man would come home, demanding that his manhood be asserted and satisfied at his wife's expense?. Were they not scared to go to bed and add to their burden every year or two.

Women should have written history and shamed the other half into reform and consideration.

1947 saw the beginning of the greatest change in the mining of coal since it had first been discovered. The advent of mechanisation took a great deal of the hard labour and drudgery out of the tasks.

Improvements were made and new methods of mining were in the vanguard. Men were treated more fairly, and conditions were drastically changed to the benefit of the work force. It hastened the closure of smaller and uneconomic units, as well as pits where life was past as a viable entity.

At the same time many mistakes were made. It was an era of hairbrained schemes. One example will suffice to illustrate this. Months were spent in an old colliery which had not progressed to conveyors, but was dependent on the old hand filling arrangements, on producing a pump in the pit bottom for pumping coal to the pit top. This entailed a great deal of excavation and the installation of expensive machinery. This was in 1954.

The time for testing drew near; it was decided to take a tub of washed coal from the surface down the pit, the coal did not reach the surface. Not quite ten cwt of coal for all that expense.

It was the time for the National Union of Mineworkers to flex its muscles, and it did that in many cases, to the detriment of all concerned. There was the feeling abroad that this was to be the Utopia for all. It was not like that. Fairness for the other persons was difficult to achieve, because the aims were diverse.

There were pits where a compromise was reached and things worked very harmoniously, but in many cases confrontation was the order of the day. Nevertheless if these two ingredients-Mechanisation and Nationalisation had blossomed early it might have been a different story.

Along with increased safety standards there were better wages. Some pits were breaking that elusive barrier and became one million ton pits. Production in mechanised units become the norm; this made for greater safety as well as far higher output.

Individual miners could quote the improvement that gave the greatest satisfaction, but the iniquity of the contracting being abolished must rank among the best. Men now worked as a team for themselves and the money was divided among them equally. As a result wages rose considerably.

This new venture was to have a limited life. Smaller pits were deemed unsuitable for modern methods as well as being past their best production days. An example of the fierceness of this can be assessed from the following figures:

From Vesting Day till 1989 nearly three hundred pits were closed. The highest figure is for 1959 when thirty two pits ceased production. From 1964 only ten were closed, and by 1972 only three. In the following eighteen years the average per year was less than two.

The complex at Longannet is the only pit in Scotland still producing coal; Monktonhall has been mothballed and faces a lot of difficulties.

We buy our coal from other countries round the world. Surely questions must be asked. What has happened to the statement made some years ago by mining authority - 400,000,000 tons of coal buried, and waits to be won for the benefit of the nation?

CHAPTER 5

DARK, DANGEROUS, BUT FUNNY

In the midst of hard labour for life, and danger, ever present and menacing, was there ever any cause for laughter and fun? You would say no; you would be wrong. Perhaps it was a safety value, a release of tension from the concentrated, physical effort of winning coal from the faceline, or making roads in heavy heard rock. It is paradoxical, but true that from this type of life and this kind of man, came a spontaneous flow of light hearted banter, and sometimes bawdy talk, that seemed to ease the burden and drudgery of the day, and made them aware, that there was more to life than grind and grumble.

Even after all this time the writer recalls a number of times when humour lightened the gloom on many a pit faceline; the quickness of the repartee never ceased to cause enjoyment and mirth, and on numerous occasions diffused situations that threatened to get out of hand.

These incidents in the main are not carried stories for most of them involved the writer, or at least was a witness, so he can truthfully say, "I was there when it happened and I ought to know."

The undermanager had two mines being driven parallel to each other, and for ventilating purposes had arranged for a small connecting road to be made. Old Jimmy and young Charlie were put on this at a given rate per fathom. The first

70

two weeks they did not make wages, and the timekeeper brought this to the official's notice who made them up to the facemen's rate. It was decided to pay them the going rate for the job for the next week.

All went well till the men got their payslips, and the old chap was soon at the door demanding a reason for the cut in wages. The official replied. "The sooner you get to know that wee Bob pays by results the better." Quicker came the man's reply. "Aye and by the look o'this payline, it's halftime results."

What would you do? Yes they were made up for the next few weeks till the job was complete. A bit of humour is better than stalemate and confrontation.

Another example about money is worth mentioning. Six men were employed at the loading area in a section, and it was quite wet with alot of water on the pavement. They were being paid sixpence each per shift, and were doing a bit of grumbling. The undermanager had agreed to go down and see the conditions, and he would give his verdict in his office at the end of the shift. There were some wags in the team and one was a fairly competent artist. This morning they were prepared for his visit. On a sheet of paper he had drawn a sketch of a man in a boat, the undermanager rowing. In the water and up to the neck in it were a number of men. The caption showed the wee man leaning over the side and saying "What do you want water money for?" The official took it down and shoved it into his pocket. At the end of the shift the men duly appeared at the office to hear the verdict, which was one of 'not proven'. The men were not pleased, and flounced out to see the manager. A few minutes later his phone rang and he was asked to go to the other office. Taking the sheet of paper from his drawer he went along. On his arrival the men were then asked to state their case again, and it was the undermanager's decision. Before he did so the undermanager showed him the piece of paper. He turned to the waiting group and said "You have proved your case, give them another tanner (sixpence)."

There were other drawings from this team and their intrepid artist. One especially relevant showed the cage landing in the pit bottom with an older man and a young lad coming down the pit for his first shift. (This was at the beginning of the close personal supervision, when a new recruit had to be accompanied at all times with a trained miner, whose job it was to ensure that the lad was given the rudiments of the job, especially with safety in mind. On this drawing there were a number of dancing wee imps with forked tails, while standing back a bit was the undermanager with his arms folded. The wee laddie on the cage has had the fright of his life; his helmet is a foot above his head, and his hair is standing on end, while his face registers sheer terror. The words on the drawing issuing from the older man's mouth. "Dinna be feart laddie, there's wee Bob the gaffer over there. It cannae be true."

One further tale comes from another drawing. This one as well as the previous ones can best be appreciated if one is acquainted with the methods of working and payments in the pits. Quite often there was a pool of trained facemen in a section who were not in the recognised team of workmen, and were called spare men, and were only required to make up the numbers if regular men were absent. This meant that these men were invariably sent to some form of oncost work which did not carry the same wage as the men on the face. Every man hated to be on the spare, for they could, and usually were sent to all the jobs that nobody wanted such as transporting heavy girders and supplies much of this done by carrying on their shoulders.

Going into section one morning the undermanagers attention was drawn to another masterpiece depicting men chained to

72

girders and to each other and the official standing back, and pointing with his stick, with the words appended. "Depart from me into everlasting oncost."

Then there was the scene where an older man was employed cleaning up the haulage road, and generally seeing that the traffic was moving freely. It was quite well on in the shift, and he was sitting in the refuge hole having a bite of piece before making his long way on foot to the pit bottom. Suddenly three men stopped beside him; the manager, the area production manager and a safety official. The top man who was renowned for his bullying, overbearing manner to all beneath him turned to the manager and barked. "Why is this man sitting eating his piece. It is not piece time and it certainly is not finishing time." Before the manager had a chance to answer, the old collier tried to explain that he always kept a half slice till this time because it was always after four o'clock before he got home with bus, and piece time was from ten o'clock till ten twenty. Disregarding the man's explanation the bossy one turned to the manager and addressed him thus. "Get this practice stopped or you will find yourself in trouble as well as this old layabout. "This proved too much for the old miner, who indignantly replied "You seem to see me sitting in the manhole, but have you seen the number of 'monkeys' on the brae that are not working. These were devices placed at regular intervals to prevent full hutches from running back down the hill if a clip slipped off the rope or the rope broke. Brusquely the inate official snarled, "I have seen a lot of monkeys since I came to the pit this morning. "Quick as a flash came the reply "Aye and they are all at the top of the tree." End of conversation.

Two men were employed driving a road, and one was sawing a prop. His shirt sleeve was flapping, and every time he bent his elbow it caught in a tear in his sleeve. His neighbour was fed up watching his antics, so he said; "Button your sleeve, man you'll soon have the shirt ruined." "I've no got any buttons on ma shirt." His mate replied." Then roll your sleeve up." "Ahm no daen that, it is faur too cold. Ah doot ah wall need to gie it away", and the other replied "You will certainly never sell it."

On another occasion the two were together, and the same man was having more trouble with his apparel. His trousers were badly in need of repair. It was at a time when a new substance had come on the market and was called No-So. This was an adhesive to take the drudgery out of sewing patches on to heavy moleskin trousers. His neighbour said to him on this occasion; "Have you not got any no-so in the house? "Yes was the reply. "I've got twenty stone of it."

It was Sunday nightshift, and five men were busy filling in the rubble blown down by the shots to pack up the sides of the roadway. Just below them Auld Matha was cleaning up the face to allow the coal cutter free passage. The youngest member of the team on the main road was on the low side just where the old man was working. His job was to fill in the dirt to form a pack to support the roof; the air was blowing down towards them. It is a unique experience to work on the wrong side of four men who have spent Sunday afternoon at a hostelry as bona-fide travellers as they were called in these days. Anyway this night the smell was terrible, and the old man and the young were often leaning over the conveyor gasping for breath; when there would be shout from the road "Anither doo away Matha. This time the shout was, "Jist a wee pickle wind." All the men were from Forth which is about eight miles from Lanark, and the prevailing wind is south west, with the bike the only form of transport. Matha had tears in his eyes when he shouted back. "Aye, and ah widnae like tae face it tae Lanark."

He was a real comic, and one night the nighshift gaffer was sending the men away to their work. Bill was instructed to go

74

to a hand pump to keep a hollow in a roadway free of water. The term in the pit for a pump that has pumped a place dry is "Snoring" Because of the distinctive sound it makes. Matha looked up at the command and winking at the rest of the men he said "There he goes and it won't be long before it is snoring and it won't be the pump.

One morning a group of men were walking home from the pit and the rain came on. One man remarked that it would be drier where he was going, and Matha affirmed "If it's no then ah'l jist draw the bed over a wee bit."

Another incident seems worthy of mention, although it was not a pit scene, but involved miners, and the pit doctor. It was Saturday morning surgery, and the waiting room was full, when there was a sudden commotion, and the local policeman entered, ushering in a man with a bad gash on his temple. The doctor took them in and immediately came out and spoke to the first man in the queue. "Come in John you are just the man for the job since you were at my first-aid class during the winter. All was quiet for a little while, and then the doctor appeared again to call the next patient, without the other men coming out with him.

The wee man followed him in and the doctor sat down in a chair and started to laugh. On recovering he said "You should have been in and seen the antics of my two assistants. I sat the man down in the chair and got the needle out to repair the damage, and had just started when the policeman pulled at my jacket and asked if he could go to the lavatory. Is something wrong I asked? He never answered and I had to rush him through the back. When I came back the miner first aider was lying below the chair; he had fainted. The patient meanwhile was sitting with a dazed look on his face. Whither it was still shock from the accident or bewilderment because of events happening around them I do not know." Later on the men were to confess that the doctor continued to rag them about the incident for a long time.

The manager was going underground one day and arranged to meet the overman to go round his district with him. At a point where two roads met, there was a seat made of wooden straps, but this one had some refinements. A back rest had been added and the whole covered with screen cloth. It must have been very tempting to tired limbs. The manager felt he should draw the overman's attention to this and to emphasise this he took a piece of chalk from his pocket, and wrote along the back "This is not a bed", and signed his name, and title and they went on their way.

The next morning he was in his office when the phone rang; this was the same official, asking him if he was coming underground that day. On being assured that he was, the man asked him if he could spare the time to come round to a bit of the pit they had covered yesterday. The two men met and soon were heading for the junction previously visited. During their walk inbye the manager asked if anything had been done about the bed. The overman said "Yes just you wait till you see the difference." They stopped at the offending seat. Below the manager's message was chalked a further addition which read as follows, "Ah ken it's no but ahm makin the best o it." Needless to say it was not signed.

Inspectors of mines are a breed apart, and carry a great deal of authority, and are carefully tended by officials, while the men invariably try to impress them with their efficiency and regard for safety.

On this occasion an overman with the manager and the inspector were crawling along a faceline, where men were filling coal on to the conveyor; this was the stripping shift. The overman was an overbearing chap, and thus not very well liked by the men. This morning he stopped beside a collier and shouted "Is this the only graith yi can get, and look at the shovel; it's broken backed." Swiftly the man defended himself by saying "Somebody has stolen mine." "Well get another set for the morn, and mind and get a bigger shovel than that. I'll no hae yi yasin a nummer fower when a seeven is whit yi shoud hae. In fact Ah hive a bigger spin for sugaring ma tea." Shouted the wild man. "Aye, replied the collier. "And wae a mooth as big as yours, you wid need it"

One day the inspector was passing along a face during the coal producing shift and stopped in a man's stint to have a rest and a talk to the miner about safety in general, and the setting of props in particular. As he sat down he leaned against a prop the man had just finished setting. (This was in the days when there were no steel props on facelines.) As he leaned back the tree fell out. After recovering from his surprise the inspector asked "Was that a permanent prop?" "Permanent nothing of the kind. It was up there tae stay," was the indignant reply.

Yes humour has its place in all kinds of situations, and is one of the outstanding facts of mining life; it is a necessary alchemy in the midst of dirt, danger and disease. It erupts in the most unlikely of places and circumstances as evidenced in the following instances.

One of the most common of accidents in the pit, in the days before gloves were accepted as normal part of your apparel, was a black nail. It was caused mainly while working at coal or stonework. It was extremely painful, and a man did not know where to put his finger. If there was water pools available this was the first resort. If not then he would clasp it in his other hand, squeeze it under his oxter (armpit) or between his legs, or in his mouth, all the while being exhorted by his mates to try another place with cruder overtones. To see a man hopping about a road going through all these antics is funny to all but the recipient, and it can be some time before the pain eases, and longer still till the nail comes off, incidentally the writer has never had a black nail having worked in Kingshill, owned by Coltness Iron Co where gloves were introduced before the last war, but were expensive to keep up at 1/6d per pair. It was not a common practice and you were invariably called piano fingers.

Accidents always bring a feeling of comradeship and help, and seemed to emphasise the common bond of miners. Men are particularly prone to take unnecessary risks to help another man trapped or in danger, and will resent steps to secure their own safety, and treat orders for such as being uncaring for the injured party, forgetting that there is little sense in losing two lives to save one. Unsupported roof has always been the main source of accidents; I speak of the days before mechanisation as we know it today.

On one occasion a man had been trapped by the hand with a fall of roof; the man was freed, and the roof made safe. In addition to a fractured finger he had lost the top of two others. There was an official to render first aid. He decided to give Jimmy some morphine. (Certain personnel were trained for this) He called Tam over to hold the injured man's hand while he gave the injection. He then prepared to carry out the task, when quietly and without any fuss, apart from a little sigh, Tam slid down the heap of coal on which he was sitting. The man with the ampoule called to the nearest man for a bottle of water, and at this there was a general cry. "Is Jimmy all right." "Of course he's all right, it's Tam that needs the water. The stupid eejits gone and fainted; You'll need to bring him roon."

Practical jokes were commonplace as well.

The old watchman had lost a leg in an accident, and was now employed on nightshift; it was in the days of the dry closets. This night he had gone to do his business, and was sitting in the appropriate place and as there was no lock on the door he had his pin leg stretched out in front of him, keeping the door shut. (It just happened that another worker was desperate and rushed up to the wee hoose and found the door shut. He could not move it, so he judged something was lodged behind it. Putting his hand round the door he felt the wood, but could not dislodge it. In his desperation he ran away to find another suitable place all the while shouting, "Whae shoved a barry ahint the shunky door."

Old Sidie a brusher on the backshift (3pm-11 pm) always had the same routine when he came home from work. Still in his pit clothes, and his carbide lamp on his cloth cap he would shout in to his wife, "Hame again hen, away to the closet." This was one of a number built alongside each other, with their attendant middens built on at the back. The dry closets were made up of spans of wood on which you sat to do your business, which in turn was open to the middens at the rear.

After he was finished he unscrewed his lamp, and knocked the bottom part which held the carbide on the pans from where it fell into the receptacle below, which in turn was open to the midden. By the very nature of the contents below the carbide gave off a gas that was very inflammable.

Some young boys through the summer nights had watched this little cameo, and had determined on some fun at Sidie's expense. Unknown to the old man they had hidden in the midden at the back, and the evening twilight, although effectively screening them, left sufficient light for them to carry out their prank.

As soon as they heard him knock out the contents of his lamp, they threw a lighted match in, and the gas ignited, burning Sidie's posterior. With a roar more of fright than pain, he leapt up, and clutching his trousers to him he ran for home crying "Help help ma erse is on fire. Send for the fire brigade." Luckily there were no serious consequences for them or Sidie, apart from the oft repeated remark; "Is your thingama still blistered."

The undermanager had spent a busy morning on a wet dirty and dangerous face where "Power Loading" equipment was being installed. At break time he crawled out on to the main road. He sat down beside a young laddie, and taking off his helmet he set about wiping his brow to get rid of the sweat and the dirt,

As he did so he noticed the young workman looking intently at him. This put him out a little, so in a brusque voice he said "What are you geikin at?" Quick was the response.. "I was just thinking if you had another wrinkle on your broo you could screw your bunnet on "You would not snarl at that remark".

CHAPTER 6

MINER FOR A NIGHT

The writer's introduction to the pit was at an early age-less than ten years. Father was nightshift at the time and often worked Saturday nights. After much persistent coaxing he got his father to arrange for him to go down with the proviso that he stay down a full shift. So kitted out with the oldest clothes that his mother could dig out, and an old pit cloth bunnet he set off to walk the two miles to the pit. Oh! The excitement; a long summer day to finish with a full shift doon the pit. What an experience it was to get on to the cage, but soon to be taken over by sheer panic as this contraption suddenly fell away, out of the evening sunshine; the summer day was quickly extinguished, giving way to an abyss of confined darkness. Did they call this thing a cage? Surely it was well named. There was no escape, and worse still no bottom to this hole through which they were hurtling. Sence and reason gave up in the face of sheer terror, and the only thing of recognisable meaning was his father's grip on his hand. He did not squeal; big boys don't cry.

What eternity's can be compressed into seconds. What emotions fill a young mind born of such an experience. It should have put him off pits for ever. It did not, for in four or five years he would have the moleskin trousers on for real.

Suddenly there was the awareness that the rope had not broken, and there was a definite drag, a slowing down, and a sudden bump stop.

There were lights too; this after Stygian darkness. There was a man there. Life was immediately marvellous, especially when the stranger spoke; "Well Matha, is this another collier yi hae brocht wi yi the nicht?" This was all night, wide and high places supported with huge girders and bricks, and there were lights everywhere; yes far better than the wee light from the carbide lamp in the cage or the paraffin lamp in the kitchen at home.

You were a man, being treated like one. What a story for the pals at school on Monday morning. Ah! But this was not the extent of the pit. After the men had a blether, while he looked round him in wonders at this new world, father and son set off along this tunnel. What had been his father's last word to the man. "See you about six." But this was only half past ten. A whole night; what would we do? He was soon to discover walk. They did not go very far along the road lined with hutches, full ones ready to go up the pit and empty ones ready for hauling in bye, when the lights ended, and they were back to the feeble carbide lamp. No recollection of much of the night is retained, except a feeling of weariness and aching limbs, broken by two incidents, the first pleasant, the other fearsome beyond words.

After they had gone for a long time, they stopped at an alcove, no it was a manhole where you took refuge when a rake of hutches passed by. There they sat and opened their piece boxes - four slices of bread - two for now and the rest for later. There was a bottle of water each to accompany the bread and jam. All things are relative, but this was an unforgettable feast. He was a man, well nearly a man with his father. Tired he might be, but give up he never would, but suddenly the road back home was much longer and bed was a mirage that was receding with every step, although it had been interesting for this man knew how to make things come alive for a laddie who hung on his every word.

84

Piece time it was called, and it did not last long, but there was a wee while to stretch out the legs and eat and drink in the middle of the night down a pit - to fit a man's experience into an hour of a boy's life, when all other chaps would be sleeping, and to do it with the one person above all others, whom you loved and worshipped, without a fear or doubt.

Too soon the respite was over, and father suggested to the boy that he should rest at this spot, while he went further in to inspect a faceline and return in about half an hour. No fear. Hastily the lad affirmed his eagerness to go all the way; did he not want to be able to say he had been everywhere in the pit when the time came for telling his adventure to the boys.

In reality he was terrified at the thought of being left alone. What if his lamp should go out? What if the roof collapsed on top of him? Or worst of all. What if his father had an accident, and could not get back to him. Horrors of great darkness he had read about, but this would beat anything you could imagine.

The final fright of the night lay just ahead. With renewed strength they went inbye together, along face lines they were called, and the point where they would finally turn and make their way back to the pit bottom, "We'll need to see how the wee pump is doing, and then we'll make for the pit bottom. At last they stopped; "Hear that noise; that's the wee pump I was telling you about." The boy was not concerned about the mechanics of a wee pump. Glad only that this was the turning point, and every step afterwards would take him nearer the lights and the company at the foot of the shaft, and surely going up could not be as bad as coming done had been.

"But where is the pump", was the query. "Doon through that hole", pointing to an opening, where a mouse would have problems. In addition it did not look safe: steel girders were bent and twisted, and the wood seemed rotten and broken. "You can't go through there, faither you'll get killt." "It will be fine; you just stay here, I'll only be a meenit or twa. You will see my light, so dinna be feart." That was it; he was the last person I wanted, to see my fear. "Ahm no feart, but it disnae look safe." After further assurance father crawled through this hole, and by the light of his lamp he saw the wee pump, and his father doing something to it-later to be explained as greasing it. He then eased himself back through the hole exclaiming as he did so; "That keeps it lubricated and it is pumping weal; the snore's fine and clean as weal, so we'll make our way back out to the pit bottom and then its hame tae the Highwid. You will not be rocked to sleep this morning, son, but before you get your breakfast, it's the bine (tub) for you to get the coal gum off you. Whit wid yir mother say if you jumped intae bed like that."

By this time he did not care about bed or bines, clean or dirty, but all his thoughts were on the fender in front of a warm coal fire; oh the luxury of stretching out along its length and going to sleep. Baths, breakfast and bed could follow later. He had his priorities right.

He knew he would be near the pit bottom when he saw the lights. Were they never to appear? He searched the roadway for some identifiable sign that it was near but there was a sameness that was confusing.

Suddenly his father said "No long noo, jist roon the next turn you'll see the lights", and so it was; he felt as if he could have run the rest of the road. Soon they were there being greeted by Wullie, and glad to rest on the wooden bench, and eat the remainder of his piece washed down by the best water he had ever tasted. It was cold and clear as this spring water down at the crusher bing on a hot summer day. "Where does it come from" He asked, and was given the reply; "It makes its way

86

through hundreds of tons of rocks from pockets of water stored in the rock above us." This enhanced its wonder and importance. He said to the two men "Jings it's better than the well doon at the den or the spring at the crusher bing"; three physical features that were to remain with him for a long time against which, thirst and its quenching were to be measured for all time.

Having finished his piece and some cups of water he lay back on the seat, and would have fallen asleep if Wullie had not said. "Ma joab is not jist to bell men up and doon the pit ah'm the pumper as weel. C'moan see if yi' hive seen pumps like this when yi' were inbye."

This was to be another chapter to add to the night's events, and tired though we was he could only stand and stare at the monstrous contraptions, while the man explained that these pumps were pumping water from there right to the surface. Was there to be no end to the discoveries of this night? While there was still a great of fear about this cage thing, with it's bars to hold you in, there was emerging in his mind the thought that it would not be so bad this time, for had not his father said so. A wee prayer would not go amiss at this point nevertheless just for safety's sake. In addition his mother's philosophy was coming through. "The first time is always the worst."

Somewhat reassured he stepped on to the cage, and a last ring of the bell, they were lifted up, and quickly whisked through the darkness, "It is no sae bad as coming doon. Yi dinnae think the thing has run away, and left yir heart in yir mooth." That is true son but there is also a difference; when you're coming up, it means your shift is finished and you are going home. Suddenly it was over: up into the light of a summer morning they rose. How you blinked your eyes to get them accustomed to the morning sunshine; but all was not over yet.

The man at the top who let us out of the cage was speaking to his father. "Matha take the laddie roon tae the enginehoose. Wullie Weir is oan this moarnin, he'llshow him roon." This was to prove the highlight of his adventure, for men were going down the pit , and it was fascinating to hear the signals and then watch as the big drums starting to revolve, and the ropes whined through a small opening in the wall, one coming in and the other going out. Soon the drums stopped. He whispered to his father "Is that them doon;" It didnae seem as long as we took."

Then if was off for home. He was tired and home beckoned. Surely the fender in front of the fire would do for a sleep first of all, Breakfast could wait. It did not happen.

"I'll let you sleep on; never mind the Sunday School the day"; suggested his mother.
"Oh no I want to go to it. I never miss it." He would not miss if for all the money in the world. He was already contemplating with glee, the envious looks in his chums eyes.
"Doon the pit at your age; my but you are lucky." He was ten years old nearly. Not much attention was paid to the Bible lesson that day. This adventure was of greater importance than anything else.......

CHAPTER 7

WEST CALDER COOPERATIVE SOCIETY

Although later than the Lanarkshire Coalmines, the shale mines and oil works in the industrial revolution ran parallel with it, during the 19th century. This lucrative field of coal covered an area of nearly eighty square miles. It stretched from the Firth of Forth, Levensea and Tarbrax in the west.

Previous to this; in keeping with its Lanarkshire counterpart, it had been a rural district, with its isolated farms and small villages, but this changed with the discovery of a certain type of coal. This would appear to be the first step in completely changing, not only the landscape, but the whole way of life for the citizens.

Exploration and exploitation started in a very primitive way. Some observant individuals had discovered that along side banks of streams and little mounds there were, in between layers of rock, this rock that was different. It could burn in a fire and was far better than wood from the woodlands all around, or peat from the less fertile stretches of moorland. This was to prove a significant step in the history of West Lothian, as an oil producing entity, and indeed, in Scotland as well, was to have far reaching consequences.

So small companies were formed. These workings were confined to small areas, and worked seams that were near the surface. Cannle coal was to play its part in this great adventure.

The word 'cannle' is named in the Concise Scots Dictionary along with other words-candles, tallow and wax. The seams of coal containing this material were often referred to; by the men working there. As working in the cannle or caunal seam.

It burned with a bright flame. This was a major experience in these early days, and a tremendous advance in the history of coal mining. Homes were now using it. It was burned in small braziers for light, and soon this was enhanced by the use of coal gas. These seams were known as gas coal seams.

As its name denotes, and as the dictionary says, it contained tallow and wax, and when burned in restorts, it produced these substances so we were introduced to the candle; a very necessary part of the household at that time.

In the preceding operations seven seams were to be worked. The thickness varied; three to seven feet seams were worked and; even one seam of nine feet in the district was known. Other seams of a few inches were not a profitable proposition.

A description of the coal-it was quite hard-gave off a distinct noise as well as a bright light when it broke up in the fire. It got the name 'Parrot coal'. As it split with the heat it sparked as well as spoke. One time it was brought to our attention was during the 1926 strike when the older men were digging for coal in the bings, the young children and the women, were gathering this gas coal from the surface of the bing.

A regular admonition by mothers as children were instructed to put on a fresh fire was a necessary precaution "See and don't put any gas coal on; it will spark out and burn someone." If you were sitting near hand or closer still, lying along the fenderstool with short trousers, and no shoes or stockings, you could feel the stinging pain where it landed.

Fortunately it sparked out in the process of kindling, or renewing a fire so it was not likely to do as much damage as a piece of coal burning in the grate. Invariably it was never fully ignited in the process and its sound and direction were easily detected. It could normally be picked up with a duster or even your bare hands.

The evolution, that had proceeded in a cautious manner from rural countryside to little pockets of population, carrying on this gradual step into urbanisation, was speeded up by the arrival of a young man from Glasgow.

James Paraffin Young by this time a world authority in oil production and new ideas.

Commercially this coal was used for oil distillation as well and the wax was also taken out during this operation. As the oil cooled this allowed the wax to crystallise. It was ripe for some adventurer. It was to prove a major discovery.

The young man from Glasgow was to prove the catalyst with his extensive knowledge and experience of oil production world wide, James (Paraffin Young.) The whole of the oil industry took off, and mines were sunk, and oil works sprang up all over the area. This brought work and wealth in abundance to the little towns and villages. Unfortunately this boom time was limited, and centres of high population were forced to face the inevitable and Tarbrax with Woolford and Cobbinshaw were in this equation. Haywood was to figure in the picture, although not in the shale mining. Its usefulness was finished at the same time.

The main reason for the collapse was the discovery of oil from indigenous wells in U.S.A. and the Middle East.
It is in this connection that Co-operatives came into being.

A number of small towns and villages, became the focal points for future development. Not only was there work for local people but there was employment for thousands. It brought about the building of houses in the area. Thus as houses became available families flooded in from other districts. It was a time of building roadways to take the increase of traffic.

Previously the small villages isolated from each other, were served by a shop in the same rows or houses as the other tenants. As the heavy industry moved into the district, more and more of these little shops were bought over, or were already run by the companies.

This could be a bad thing, because there were instances, where a man's livelihood; indeed, the well being of his family, depended on his wife buying in the work owners' shops. If she did not patronise the company shop a man could find himself threatened with the sack, or a downgrade in his wages. Not only so but if you did not toe the line at your work, your wife would find the effect quickly felt when she was refused provisions. Your name would soon find its way into the realm of other owners. It was a no win situation.

An interesting example was a fairly modern happening in the Lothians where Mungo Mackay held supreme sway over the town of Newtongrange, and its surrounding villages.

This made the right conditions for the setting up of the Cooperative movement on a fairly wide scale.

It was fertile ground for the introduction of Co-op Societies. As communities grew up around the pits and works, these stores played an important part in the development of the villages. One has called it the early aim of providing an alternative union of working men for the improvement of the social

92

circumstances of the class to which they belong; it is man's lever by which he may rise in the world. It was to be a means of breaking the feudal system.

West Calder was the first to break this mould, in that it was entirely in the hands of workmen from its commencement. It was not the first cooperative when it was opened in 1875. Uphall and Oakbank were opened in 1872 and 1873. The life of all these cooperatives depended on the life of the adjacent works.

The West Calder shop was opened after a strike in the local pits following its unsuitable conclusion, there was an abandonment of the unions. Some forty men, with more foresight than the rest, decided to withdraw, and take their share of disbanded union's funds. They decided to use their share of the proceeds -£70 to start this adventure. It did not prove in vain. In the first year there were sixty members and sales totalled £2,305. By 1893 sales had risen to £21,761 while members were now at 412.

By 1903 the figures were vastly increased; there were 572 members and sales stood at £30,866. Obviously the society had expanded greatly; branches being formed at outlying places like Cobbinshaw, Blackburn, Tarbrax and Haywood. Forth was to be started in 1925. Other cooperatives which had been separate stores were also taken over during this expansion period.

It soon developed beyond the original groceries and provisions. As well as having a branch in the villages this was augmented by the use of vans bringing bakery, fleshing, milk, rolls, drapery and hardware as well as oil for the miner's rows.

Sales per family CO. Book did not seem to be very high. West Calder in 1883 had sales per household of £58, and over the years did not seem to rise much above this figure. Again this must be the fact of low wages among miners and other manual workers.

It had far more van trade than the others, and this in great measure was responsible for higher sales. The factor of the dividends must be considered. Prices in general were higher than the local privately owned shops. This was raised as an argument against it, but the opponents had to concede that the paying of the dividend was, according to another, an incentive towards thrift for those who do not know how to save; far less how to spend.

The writer's mother was a good person as the exchequer of the household; she was never known to go past the 'Co' for anything, with the Co book being squared every Saturday morning without fail, from Friday's pay packet. So the dividend was kept in the Co till the end of the quarter when dividends were paid out. Another benefit, was the fact that any money saved, could be used to purchase extras like footware, clothes and other bigger articles. If it was not needed for this, it could go on to your share book, and this was indeed a method of saving.

During the boom period of the oil extraction West Calder's population increased, and by the time of the World War it stood at 3000, while 10,000 men were employed supporting at least 40,000 in the whole of the Lothian region.

It was also the time of enlarging of the Co. Boundaries; other country villages, with only one real drawback, that of Cobbinshaw, which only existed for one year, Tarbrax continued as a going concern till well on into 1950's Mrs Muir (Robertson) was manager up till that time. It started in 1892, while its neighbouring one at Cobbinshaw started in 1899.

A village was built at Tarbrax in Lanarkshire around the oil works, and by 1900 these had been modernised and extended. Water was piped into the houses at this early date, which says much for the foresight and modern planning. This was a direct contrast with Haywood which never had any facilities up until the village was finished in 1930's. The houses at Tarbrax have been bought mainly by sitting tenants and the community is still as thriving as ever it was; the only drawback is the fact it is now a commuter base for places as far apart as Glasgow and Edinburgh, with Livingston, the nearest developed area.

The facilities still retained include a tennis court, bowling green, indoor bowls as well as other winter activities. These have the enthusiastic support of the village people, but visitors are frequently seen about the village. You will be assured of a warm welcome, if every you find time to visit. I speak from experience.

It says much for the spirit of the older folks who have kept it alive, although there is a growing tendency for the workers commuting long distances, and stressful conditions at work, to have less time and energy for socialising. Nevertheless the advent of young people has prevented it from becoming a ghost of pensioners. What a contrast it is from its neighbours Cobbinshaw and Haywood, although Woolford was spared when Cobbinshaw was demolished. Indeed the row of houses still remain. They to, have been up graded.

The Cooperative in Haywood (the Store,) as it was designated, opened in 1894 on Christmas Day..This was after a lengthy delay and some strong arguments about the site. Tashyburn was in the running, but finally rejected, because it was too far from the village, although equidistant to the two places.

Undoubtedly; one of the main reasons for the difficulty, was the resentment of the landlords to make a situation available for a Cooperative. This attitude was further supported by local proprietors of other shops.

A way out of this dilemma was found, when the Right Honourable Akers Douglas. M.P who owned considerable parts of the village, being approached by his agent, consented to allow sufficient ground to erect premises. A site was taken in September 1894 and buildings completed and stock provided, ready for opening on Christmas Day of the same year.

An account of this ceremony was given in the Lothian Courier.
"The premises, although not large, are so arranged that a large trade can be done with comparative ease." The opening ceremony was performed by the President Mr James Potter; the whole of the committee being present.

After a few remarks to a crowd of members, by the vice president and others, the door was opened by a sliver key, which was presented to the president by the building contractor, Mr John Fairley. The Business done at this branch of the West Calder Cooperative Society has been highly satisfactory. Mr James Blair was its first manager. This same man was one of the stalwarts, along with the Rev.Gilbert Clark of the Boys Brigade, being second lieutenant with the minister as captain.

Jeanie Weir and Miss Martha Murdoch were there at the end of its days.

If in earlier times there were three places of real moment, the coming of the Co made a welcome addition. The focal points were Hughie Dunn's licenced grocer down at the square; the village hall and Kechan's at the top of the hill. These shops were essential 'Adults Only.' Except when messages were required at the two shops or in the hall, if there were special events for children. The Co became the main rendezvous for the women folk. No wheeled trolleys and check outs. You waited your turn and as you waited you were supplied with news of the village, while you relayed your bits of information. This was the proper place to put the people and the world to rights.

The life of the Cooperative was governed by the money earned in the pits. When this ended: there was no need for messages and no money so with the collapse of the village the Co died as well, although it was in the thirties that it finally closed. All the trade went to Forth where a shop had been opened in 1925.

An excerpt from the Courier Newspaper dated 11-11-07 records the details of 129th Quarterly Meeting of the West Calder Co-operative Society. In this there is a recommendation from the Committee:

"That powers be granted them to purchase property for further extension of premises at Tarbrax, and that the cost of same be taken out of the 'Reserve Fund; was then brought forward. The chairman said that since the opening of the branch, the trade had increased by leaps and bounds, and at the present time the premises were too congested for the trade done. They had received an offer from the Tarbrax Oil Company of the Institute Hall, which is part of the building wherein the premises were presently situated, for £450 and if the members sanctioned the purchase, the hall could be fitted up as a good grocery shop, and the present grocery shop made into a butcher's shop. They estimated the cost of alterations at £350. After a little discussion the vote was taken and resulted-for the recommendation 209 against 13."

In an article carried on 8-5-25 there is the account of the Quarterly Meeting of the members of the West Calder

Co-operative Society Jubilee Celebrations. The committee recommended that a souvenir be presented to every member to the value of 5s on the occasion of the Society's Jubilee and that the cost be deducted from the Reserve Fund.

Mr Pratt said the Jubilee year was a most important one to members. Two years ago he recommended that 3d per £ of sales be put aside to meet expenses in connection with the celebrations of the Jubilee. Mr Pratt gave a very full statement of the various suggestions put forward for commemorating the Jubilee. The recommendation of the committee was a practical one in which all members would participate. They proposed to give each member a souvenir to the value of 5s and that he cost be met out of the Reserve fund. He hoped the member would support the committee's recommendation.

After a lengthy discussion and a vote the recommendations of the Jubilee were adopted

A Branch for Forth.

The committee recommended that powers be given to purchase property or erect buildings for branch premises at Forth at an estimated cost of £4000. Mr Pratt made a full and clear statement regarding the call for the proposed branch at Forth, from which district the Society had been petitioned to open a branch twelve years previously. The causes of the delay were clearly set out, and, in view of the statement put before the meeting he urged that the committee's recommendation be upheld. It had been supported all over the branches and he hoped it would be at the Central. Recommendation of Committee was unanimously agreed to.

Jubilee of West Calder Co-operative Society - Courier 19-6-1925

"West Calder Co-operative Society which has a membership of nearly 9000 celebrated its Jubilee on Saturday. The Society started in a very small way in 1875 with a capital of £70, and the sales now exceed £500,000 per annum. The first premises comprised a small shop in the main street of West Calder and when the first consignment of goods was bought the committee spent all night unpacking them and displaying them in the shop. Today the Society has extensive central premises and a fine suite of offices in West Calder and branches at Midcalder East Calder; Purpherson, Uphall Deans, Blackburn, Stoneyburn, Addiewell, Haywood and Tarbrax. To mark the occasion the Society gave a donation of £1000 to the funds of Edinburgh Royal Infirmary and £100 to the Co-operative Convalescent Homes. Each member was presented with a souvenir gift to the value of 5s and an illustrated history of the Society. The children were also presented with a souvenir."

The final episode in this important piece of history is contained in the Courier 8-7-77

Landmark to go say planners.

West Calder Co-op is to be demolished-and that looks like being the last decision on the building.

"So the curtain runs down on one of the most successful ventures by a group of men under very trying circumstances, and in its time served communities where ever Paraffin Young and others made towns and villages."

CHAPTER 8

MAPS

In an overall survey throughout the last few centuries of the small area of the Upperward of Lanarkshire it is evident that originally the land in and around it was poor quality and in the main was quite infertile. Observations made in early days prove this to be the case, but to offset the bareness of the ground, was the wealth of minerals below it. There were great quantities of coal iron and limestone with an abundance of rich sand deposits.

The Union of 1707 saw a great change in the character of Scotland. Machinery in farming was gradually taking over from the old hard working methods; industry was commencing, so the urbanisation of cities, towns and villages took place over a long period. Thus in the highlands this practice was expedited by tenants being cleared of their lands to make room for sheep.

Large areas were required for this exercise e.g. Sutherland estate which was made up of small farms and crofts, was cleared of its population.

Some were offered holdings on narrow strips of land adjoining the sea and therefore were obliged to make a living in an environment to which they were foreign-mainly fishing.

There were other outcomes of this. Emigration began on a large scale; America and Canada were the favourites with Australia and New Zealand not far behind. This was a great service in the building of the Great British Empire. No one will deny that the skills of Scotland were a major factor in this. But this must have been a brain drain, that would be severely missed in the homeland.

Added to this was the continual drift of dispossessed people to the industrial belts of Scotland and England. To this must be added the setting up of Highland Regiments. Men flocked to enlist in the army, conned by the widespread lie that this was the best for everyone.

There are examples of inhabitants of Haywood being born as far away as Skye Lairg and Inverness. This is shown in the 1891 census. So the clachans were denuded and many lonely glens and straths, still bear the evidence of a way of life long since gone-stone built ruins left, like Haywood, to the ravages of wind and weather.

The defeat at Culloden played a tremendous part in this slide into oblivion as a nation. Another atrocity of this long hard period was the burning of houses with the tenants still in them. How can history like this ever be forgotten nor forgiven?

Another parallel happening at this time was the regular influx of Irish men and women upsetting the way of life for a mainly Presbyterian populace. This is borne out by the census of 1891 also. This migration was caused by worse atrocities than in Scotland. It is also noted in the same census that fifty eight men and women had been born in Ireland. Unfortunately only in a few instance was the town of birth mentioned; viz. John Feely-Donegal, J.Finess-Antrim, M.Donaldson-Donegal, Cecilia Murray-Sligo. It might be of interest to some who have connections with the village, to know if they have Irish ancestors who came to live in Haywood.

It must be noted that there is only one man mentioned from Wales-John Jones-Blanwern. There is no mention of any from England apart from John Smith. One women was born in New York but is given as a British subject.

Another date that was to have major significance, the 1745 rebellion and its final battle at Culloden. Men who had fought and had escaped, as the nation slid down into oblivion as a nation.

The English authorities and the Hanoverian line gained a twofold victory. They got rid of a difficult people who were dangerous to the powers that be; men who had been ferocious foes and pariahs were in the then future, hailed as heroes, at the knock down price of the King's Shilling. Would the old Scots proverb fit this case? There are many ways of killing a cat than by feeding it cream!

One authority of the day put it more bluntly 'It solves the problem of irascible men who were a plague to the nation now proving to be a sound investment as a fighting force in support of the Empire, and its expansion. If they are killed at the forefront of the battles we'll laud them and give them a heroes burial and erect a few monuments to their memories'.

Kind David of Israel was not the last leader to employ devious methods to get rid of a nuisance and a threat to his career and advancement, when he gave the order to his ruthless generals 'Set Uriah at the front of the battle and leave him isolated by a strategic withdrawal.' David had of course a sound reason for this. He had committed adultery with Uriah's wife when the man was at the front fighting for the king.

Another order had been given previously; give him a weekend pass to be with his wife'. His order was obeyed and the brave soldier got compassionate leave on the regal authority. Did Uriah smell a rat or was his excuse genuine. 'I will not go to my home for a night's pleasure but will spend it in the Lord's house. Praying for victory for my king and country.' Hence the king's reason for acting. The whole thing followed the whispered words of Bathsheba on the housetop to David. 'I am pregnant.' The decision not to see his wife on his leave had thrown all the King's plans to the wind. David found a way to get rid of his problem. Get the man killed and no one would ever know. It would be his and his lover's secret.

In the Scottish case the same brand of deviousness is evident.

But our purpose is not to look at the wide aspect as only a small area was affected. A study of some maps of these centuries - I am indebted to the Map Dept. National Library in Edinburgh for the use of these-will help to give a true picture of the rise and fall of a district and especially of one now lonely village.

In many ways it epitomises the trend of the years. All over the land towns with rich engineering, mining, and industrial prospects attracted the necessary labour, so ghettos became firmly established, and overcrowding and slum conditions were rampant, as families fought for a living wage. A look at the housing and conditions as depicted for the 1891 census will bear that out. Indeed it is within living memory that the rows in Haywood were not upgraded in any way apart form the need to increase the living accommodation; It is for this reason, that if the size of the family became so great, that a single end, could not contain them, increased space became available by the simple task of waiting till the family through the wall in their single end moved out, then knocking a hole in the wall and fitting a door.

103

Perhaps it was realised that the life of the village would be short so why should the company go to the expense of doing anything to the houses. It was good enough for them. The coal owners were not made of money, so sacrifices had to be made, and you started where it could be most easily bourne. This was the era of the tied house system.

There is a better known High Wood as depicted in a piece written by Phillip Johnstone.

Ladies and Gentlemen this is High Wood.

Called by the French Bais De Tourreaaex,
The famous spot which in 196
July, August and September was the scene
Of long and bitterly contested strife;
By reason of its high commanding site.

Observe the effect of the shell fire in the trees
Standing or fallen; here is the wire, the trench
For months inhabited; twelve times changed hands,
(they soon fall in) later used as graves.
It has been said on good authority
That in the fighting for this patch of ground
Were killed somewhere above eight thousand men
Of whom the greater part were buried here.
The mound on which you stand being......Madame please
You are requested kindly not to touch
Or take away the Company's property
As souvenirs; you'll find we have on sale
A large variety, all guaranteed.
As I was saying, all is as it was.
This is an unknown British Officer
The tunic lately rotted off
Please follow me - this way.......the paths Sirs please.

The ground, that was secured at great expense:
The company keeps absolutely untouched
And in the dug out (genuine) we provide
Refreshments at a reasonable rate.
You are requested not to leave about
Paper or ginger bottles or orange peel
There are wastepaper baskets at the gate.

Phillip Johnstone

There were cases of land owners receiving more per ton of coal produced than the men who were at the point of the pick. Market forces were applicable then, but there must be some truth in the article in the Scotsman of 28-8-96 by David Blunket. He said "If you have a tiny minority going to university, by their very nature they will be brilliant. Some feel this trickles down, what I call the aristocratic incontinence - the belief that if a small elite do very well their gains, their wealth, their privileges, will trickle down to the rest of us. I don't accept that for a moment." He says.

Past experience in nearly two hundred and fifty years has proved the truth of what he says. It was not true in these far off days; it was not true even in the hyped up days of the Thatcher years, and it is still not true.

We go back to the development and demise of Haywood by looking at a number of maps during the period 1654-1913 - some of which, where practicable, are reproduced here.

1654-Vpperward of Clyds-Dyl - J.Blaea. (not shown) This is the earliest map held by the Map Dept of the National Library of Scotland of this area we are considering. (Copied from Blaeu's Atlas 1x42.) Local places are mentioned e.g W Forth, E Forth, Crukends, Kaerburran Law, Haywood and

105

Cleugh-with Cobinfhaw the furthest east. Kalder Moore between us and west Calder with Athkar Moore situated between Forth and Shotts (Muldron). Two other places that have not seen much change apart from the spelling of their names: Auchingre and Carfwat. These are obviously Auchengray and Carnwath. Incidentally Auchengray celebrated its centenary a few years ago. A video was made of this occasion and makes excellent viewing. The extensive moors are vital proof that the whole area was quite infertile.

1773-Map of the Shire of Lanark-Charles Ross.(shown),
Moutainblow, Highwood and Crooklands, note new spelling of Crooklands which it retains till this day, although in our young days we always called it Crukens. It is of note that the village was named as Highwood. This is the only map that carries this name. Again local people never said anything but Highwid. Crimpie is shown near Forth and there appears to be two places called Tarbrax. The Lang Whang A71 is shown but the name is not used.

Mouse Water is noted, but near its source it is called Cleughburn; just below the Cleugh estate where it splits into two. This branch is shown as flowing south of Moutainblow and the other north of the farm. The former tributary is obviously the Kaerburran but its route is not quite true, or the position of the village is wrong. The course of this burn in the years of my childhood did indeed start up near Moutainblow but it flowed down past Haywood head and the mine cottage and on to the old pit bing what we knew as the Crusher bing and it was known then as the Law Burn.

There is no road between Haywood and Auchengray and Carnwath, but there is one from Carnwath to Forth and Crimpie with a connection to Shotts over Athkar Moore. This divergence was at Stobie and Stobiehill. The other leg continued on
106

to Forkens later known as Wilsontown (after the iron foundry owner). White Loch - a favourite dooking place for us when bikes became an everyday means of transport.

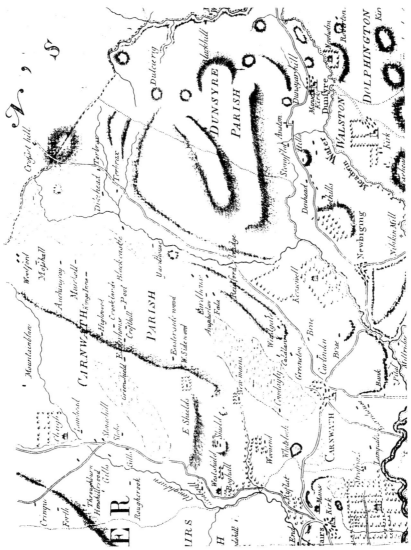

1773-Map of the Shire of Lanark-Charles Ross.

107

1816 County of Lanark - Wm. Forrest. (not shown) Cobbinshaw - note change of spelling - before it was called Cobbinshaw bog. This was before it was a man made loch to supply water for the Edinburgh and Clyde Canal Dippool, Clark's Walls (Ruins). We called this the den down beside the old farmhouse. We carried the water from this point to our home at the top of the village. Auchengray assumes its new name.

The Drove Loan passes through the village on its way south from the markets at Falkirk and Crieff. A sheep house is shown nearby. This would be an overnight stop for tired men, dogs, and animal herds.

Bencurin Hill lies east of Levenseat with Tormy Wheel in between-this appears to be a couple of raised points but its name may have some connection with industry.

The sheep and cattle road passes west of Moutainblow then down through Bughtknowes to Clark's walls and on to the Hardgatehead and Pool farms. We walked this part of it when I was younger; before age and the fear of peer groups would let you know the next morning at school. 'He was out a walk with his mamy.'

Haywood and Greenbank are separate entities while Tashyburn, Harry Foothill and Burnfoot are included.

Mention is also made of the Iron Works- iron lime stone with coal mines.

Wilsontown House (home of the Wilson family.) after whom the village of Wilsontown was named. Previously it had been called Forkens. There was a mine driven into the hillside some distance from Dixon's pit and connected to it by an endless haulage hutch track. See 'Romance of Wilsontown." By P.M Ritchie Managing Director of Wm. Dixon Coal Co.

108

Haywood Burn flows past Crookers. We knew this as the station burn. The railway line was its course before the water emptied into the Dippool between Haywood and Auchengray. No road is inserted between the two villages. Indeed up till the present there is only an unclassified road and it is seldom used.

In 1822 John Thomson Bencurrin Hill and, Tormy hill are again included and Cobbinshaw is still a bog. Drove Loan still exists. Wilsontown House, Iron Works, Climpy House, and this appears to be the first note of a chapel of rest. There are Lime and Coal works as well as lime iron and sand quarries. Cleugh Mill and W.M and E. Forth with an interesting inclusion; Crukern Inn at the junction of the Forth Lanark and the Forth Carnwath road has long passed into oblivion. Around this time there appears to be a lot of industry going on in the district with a small railway from Wilsontown to Muiraw and the coal pits beyond. This would be an evidence of the boom years at the end of the eighteenth century and the beginning of the nineteenth.

Rotten Burn is shown. This is an offshoot of the Mouse near Pleasance Row and where Calder Terrace was built. It has long since been demolished as has Quality Row which overlooked the works, but Burnside cottage still is occupied. This is on the waters edge where the two streams meet. There is still no sign of a road between Haywood and Auchengray

1859 O.S Lanarkshire Sheet xx. (Edition of 1913 as revised shown).
Caledonian Railway, Edinburgh and Carstairs passes through Auchengray and Carnwath. Appended to this line is an Electric Telegraph. The line from Auchengray to Haywood and Wilsontown has not been built. (If the railway had come earlier it might have halted or prolonged the demise of the flourishing iron works.

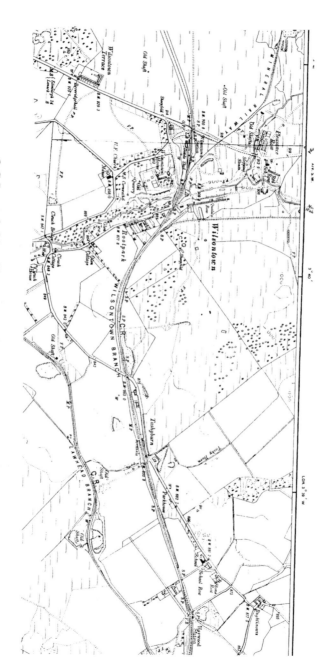

O.S Lanarkshire Sheet xx. (Edition of 1913 as revised)

The death of the works must also have affected the mines, because no working mines are recorded. A tram is shown leading from Mill Dam to Oldmill and Millhill: the brick works at Auchengray flourishing at this time. There are thirteen disused pits in Tashyburn and Haywood, twenty two in the area comprising Climpy, The Abbey, Forth, Beveridge Hall and Greenwell.

In a small excerpt from a larger map eleven rows are mentioned while the census for 1891 gives at least twenty three. This map of 1910 gives an insight into the core of the village of Haywood. The names of the rows are as follows; Store Row, Bank Street, Lorne Street, Princess Street, Ann Street, Park Street.

One personal note of limited interest to the reader is the mention of stepping stones over the Mouse near the junction of the two streams. These were handy when travelling to and from school. It saved a journey round by the Store Close, the Red Row, old and new schools, and the Pleasance.

When you were bigger you felt superior to the small fry if you could race down the path and jump the burn. It cut your time by a few seconds. I never remembered walking home from school at dinner time. Going back a different matter; no need to hurry you were only going back to school while on the outward journey you were going for a meal, and you were starving.

I cannot remember the record time, although it was checked every day with the clock in the home. Enjoyable it was and good training for the Gala day and the Sunday School trips. These stones were well worn and must have been used for a long time and by many feet.

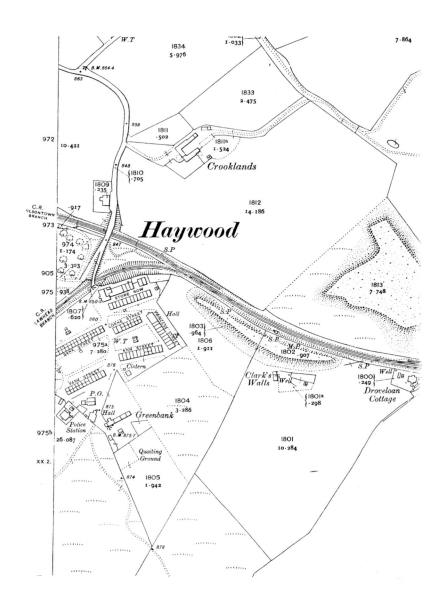

O/S extract Lanarkshire 1910

112

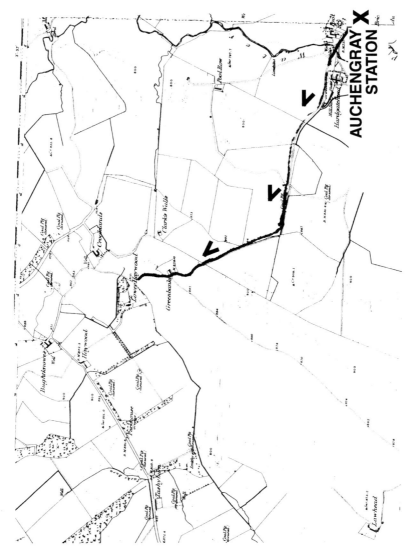

Life's Cruelty; Deaths Release.

The Caledonian Railway passenger service stopped at Willsontown but the line carried on to Climpy pit and later to Kingshill pit while two branches ran to the right; one to the east of Quality Row serving No. 9 pit. The other went to Dixon's pit on the East.

On this map there are shown churches and manses in the district. One interesting feature shows the presence of a Mission Hall at the lower end of Forth Main Street. This became known as the wee kirk. The Boys Brigade met here during my days as a member and if finance could stretch to the penny entrance fee. This too had to be subsidised when Rev.Mr John Rae held occasional lantern lectures. Mention of this Christian gentleman brings back memories of time spent in Roadmeetings Hospital. There had been quite an epidemic of diphtheria in Forth and district. About a dozen were in hospital for four weeks. Mr. Rae visited the hospital once very week with comics fruit and sweets. He used his old upright bike for the journey. I can vouch for the truth of the fact that you did not need to be a member of his church. This Christian gentleman was among the most loved and respected persons the villagers have every known.

The Geographical Survey of Scotland 1878, shows the extent of mining operations at this time from Haywood to Pool and Hardgatehead. The Main coal was fairly near the surface,; depths varying from 6, 7, 16, 17, 19, 20, 27, fathoms. Rising due East broken by an upthrow fault there is an outcrop between Hardgatehead and Pool.

Number of pits still working main coal = 4
Number of pits still working gas coal = 2

There appears to be only one working both seams while there is only mention of one disused pit.

In the Haywood and Tashburn area one pit is working gas coal. Other four are down to the main seam. In the Forth and Climpy section there are no pits working and eighteen are disused.

From these figures it might well be assumed that this area was last to be exploited, while the closure of the iron works at Wilsontown had undoubtedly led to the end of the nearby pits. It is of interest to note that two pits No.5 and No.9 were working at the turn of the century. (See Reminiscence of Haywood.) Now the bings themselves are disappearing, as they are being used as bottoming for roads etc. One new road was laid recently from Mine Cottage on to the course of the old line to work out the opencast near Burnfoot and Auchengray Junction. This road is now closed to public transport, a gate at the north end being padlocked. Another open cast in the moors adjoining Climpy. It too has gone.

The seams being near the surface, access was not difficult although water was a problem. No pits now, since Kingshill and Dixons finished. One mine in production.

CHAPTER 9

CULTURAL SHOCK.

Culture. not many in a mining village would understand much about this word. (Collins English Dictionary and Thesaurus) gives the meaning:-

1. The total of the inherited ideas, beliefs, values and knowledge, which constitute the shared basis of social activity.
2. The total range of activities and ideas of a people.
3. The artistic and social pursuits, expressions and tastes valued by a society or class.

People came from a wide area, therefore they would bring much of their own way of life with them, but it would be difficult for someone from Inverness, possibly speaking the best English in the whole of Britain to come to a foreign part which spoke neither English nor Scots, but a hotchpotch of both. Take it further, and think of a new young wife in her single end in the row, greeting her neighbour the morning after the flitting to be met with the response. "Never mind hen; div yi think yi like it here. Were aa Jock Tamsons' weans. Nae high falutin' airs and graces wi'us. Yi'll jist need tae tak us as yi'finn us." This might be termed a cutural shock. Another outstanding case, more extreme than the former; a man born in the south of Ireland speaking both Gaelic and English with an Irish accent, finished up marrying a beautiful lassie born in Islay. She too speaks the two languages he knows. Where did they meet? How did they meet? The fact that none of the family spoke Gaelic or English would suggest that they soon fitted in with the talk of the rows as well as pit talk. They had two boys and two girls. It would be a very difficult decision to make; to move on or stay.

When they arrived the family would have doubts about the wisdom of the decision. They never would settle down; this would break their spirits. It says much for the resilience of the newcomers; this indomitable attitude would soon become noticed by the locals, as they settled down: accepting circumstances as they were. You certainly could not change them.

The sad thing about it was they did accept the spirit of the place and time. Many; instead of nurturing their own way of life too readily fell into the trap of accepting, and tholing, the existing conditions. It was very difficult to maintain your individual identity when all around was so ingrained with a low estimation of your own part in the scale of things.

A mining village with its rows of houses might bring back memories of a crisp winter evening, with the smoke from fresh fires, rising straight up into the night air. It was a welcome sight when viewed from the raised paths and road into it. It told of the miner's backs being washed before a bleezing open fire; its heat spreading warmly through the kitchen, and the soup pot hanging on the swee, soon to be ladled into numerous plates on the table. Not only so, but there would be the vision of boiling beef and tatties to follow or mince and tatties. When all this was finished, it was time to make up the fire, and as this action took place in every home around the same time, twenty three rows of houses would produce a fair amount of smoke. To memory it did not seem dirty, but light against the sky. It lay like a grey blanket above. It looked braw and gave a pleasant air of community and relationship.

A reeky dirty hole would more usually be a fitting description. It would be viewed like that by strangers, newly come from the wide open spaces of the island of Islay or Ireland.

The hills of the north, and the rolling uplands of the south would be hard to forget. Apart from the fact that it was in the upperward, its main and important raised ground was not green sided mountains but bings getting ever higher, as the days' detritus was spewed from the underground to leave pockmarks like a garrison, to keep the prisoners in safe custody. These were to have a beneficial effect in years to come when strikes would ensure that the men who built these same bings would reap a bonus when they dug in them for stray coal to keep the fires going until the men went back to work, to replace that which was taken away.

Looking at the position from the incomer's angle, the morning would be heralded in by the blaring horn at the pit rousing men and women from warm beds. This would soon be followed by the starting horn summoning men to the pit, and women did not need horns. Many never used alarm clocks.

As many of the pits were close by, the noise in the homes would be a constant irritant, and the smoke and dust would help along, the incidence of coughing and lung disease; the terms silicosis (stone dust) and pneumoconiosis (coal dust) were terms for a different and later age.

Refinement and polish were conspicuous by their absence Advancement from the rut would only be accomplished by pulling yourself up by the boot laces, or by trampling others underfoot, in your endeavours to escape. Money or rather the lack of it was the force that ruled the roost. People were poor.

Having said that it did not quench the spirit of kindness and sharing. "Serve'sma. Serves'aa."

118

The settling in period would not be easy but over against it must be acknowledged that the two sides were bound by the same bonds. They had to get on together, if life was to have any significance and worth. They each buckled down to the job.

After the initial meeting, an acknowledgement of the mining spirit would make sure the wives and weans were given every opportunity to make a go of things. This initiation was crude and basic, but generally kindness was the alchemy that bonded them together.

A similar transformation would take place in the pits. Ribald miners were always ready to make fun, at the efforts of ex-farm workers and labourers, but gradually the novices would be assimilated into the working order of the mine. It would not be smooth and gentle, but rough and rugged. There was also the fortunate one who landed with a mate, more caring and helpful, than the rest. He was a lucky man who landed with a miner of this kind.

Many of these jobs were at the coal face, so the greatest part of the shift was spent on your knees.

Eight hour shift was spent on your knees or side depending on the height of the working. It was easy; your tools were simple. It comprised a shovel pick and a mash. Height, or the lack of it, could be eighteen to twenty four inches.

You could opt out for the job with less money. It was called drawing-not of water like the Israelites of long ago-but of hutches. As the face man won the coal, he threw it out onto the road, where it was handfilled into a hutch. The drawer then pushed it out quite a distance to be coupled up with the rest of the hutches. From that point rakes of hutches were hauled out to the pit bottom. In early mining this was done by horses with a pony laddie in change. Humane measures freed the animal from this ever lasting darkness. Some of these horses never saw daylight. They died in the pit.

It might be of interest that ponies were still being used in a pit in the Lothians at least until 1954. Now, except in a few cases, men have been withdrawn as well.

In the days of what was termed hand drawing, roads were, for economical reasons, driven to suit the dimensions of a hutch-four to five feet high and the same for width. It was a cramped place of work. Some hands and arms were common as were feet and legs, but backs had the worse treatment. Knotted scabs were a well recognised feature as your back was all the time rubbing on the roof or wooden bars to support it. If this was not the only way to get a sore back you could get a change of injury by racking it, when lifting a loaded hutch, that had gone off the rails.

It was brutal work aggravated by lack of good ventilation in many cases in the confined darkness. This was worsened when shots were fired and dense clouds of smoke filled the air.

The consternation would be real if the man was injured and he appeared at the door of his home with a makeshift bandage round his arms or legs. The worse fright for his wife, would be the day he turned up at the door with a dirty bandage on his head. Safety helmets were not invented, and as one wag put it "You wid be as weel wi' a happeny stamp on yir heed, fur aa the guid thae wee claith bunnets did yi." What a change from the freedom of the open air.

The daily drudgery of the housewife might be broken by the shout from next door on a summer morning. Calling you to have a cup of tea and a crack on the doorstep-a welcome break-

"The teas maskit time for a blow." Neighbourliness has always been a product of kindred spirits facing the same unenviable life in the rows. The following story will illustrate this.

CHAPTER 10

NEW BEGINNINGS

Mary had been born on the Island of Islay. She spoke Gaelic and English and had been brought up in a small croft during the first fifteen years of her life. She had left when the younger members were able to take over some of her work.

This move was hastened by the plea from relatives near Oban that they needed help with their farm. She was to spend the next four years with them. The work proved to be hard and unrewarding; she had expected a home like her own but instead she was treated like a slave. How she longed for home; to be back in the warmth and comfort of the little family circle.

This changed dramatically when she was sent over to another place to help with the harvest. This was only a temporary measure. It was accepted at this time, that when the harvest was gathered in the roles were reversed.

She enjoyed the experience very much. The stern kindness was readily appreciated, and she was happier than she had been for a long time. The three weeks had flown, and it was with regret that she said goodbye to her employers. Perhaps the main reason for her happiness was the presence of a young farm labourer. She could not believe her good fortune when she was told that he was to see the harvest in at her place.

Long days in the field were compensated by the walk in the summer gloaming. One great experience that remained with her was the night she rode home on the Clydesdale's back. They had worked hard in the fields all day and well into the evening. It was too good weather to stop because morning might bring rain. He saw her weariness as they left the field and so without prompting he lifted her on to Dinah's back. She could feel the tingle of his hands as he touched her and was glad of the gloaming to hide the flush on her face. She had enjoyed his company so much, although the work was heavy.

Another thing that created a bond between them was the fact that they both spoke Gaelic. His was not quite the same as hers but they soon learned. His accent being Irish was funny at first. The learning was wonderful and it had the added joy; they could shout in secret to each other.

The young man from Ireland felt that this was what heaven would be like, and soon he asked her to marry him. She listened then she started to produce obstacles, but these were quickly repudiated by her suitor. Her final answer brought the family into the frame.
"I will need to go back and take you with me to get their permission before I can marry you. Will you get away from your work for a day or two?"
"I will, or I will leave and get another fee with someone else. I'll will ask Jimmy and his wife. I am sure they will give me time off for such an important occasion. Jenny has been dropping the hints it was time I made up my mind about my intentions, so she will be well pleased."

She became quiet. "What will my relations say? I have worked for them as hard as anyone could these last three years. They will not want to part with me. Because I am sure that they'll never get anybody to work for the pittance that I get. May ain folks will not be keen to see their lassie married to an Irishman."

The first obstacle was overcome. He was free to go with her on the first free weekend after the harvest was finished. They decided not to inform her parents in case they would not let her associate with an Irishman; especially one who was six years older.

They followed this plan and arrived at her parents home on a Saturday night. What a day it had been; sitting close together. They had never been on their own like this before. Emotion as they saw the island from the front of the ship; its flat greenness contrasted with the bare Paps of Jura.

Soon they were at Port Askaig. It was only a short distance to home; about four miles. It was a walk of delight. Stopping for a kiss and a cuddle was a frequent event and could not be hurried. Yet as they neared home she become quieter. He suffered as well.

She said "Do you think they will let us in when they see you with me?"
"Of course they will. You are their daughter." He did not feel as cheery as his confident words sounded.

They were at the door. "Kiss me quickly." She whispered "I am frightened for us."

She knocked tentatively and then pushed open the door. A meal was set on the table, father, mother and two brothers and her young sister enjoying the evening meal.

She startled them by calling "It is Mary home to see you." The chairs scraped on the flag stones, as they all leapt to their feet. Mother was first to respond, but in the act she noticed her daughter was not alone. She hesitated, then took her lassie in her arms, but even as she did so, the look on her face betrayed

124

the fact that she had seen the man in the shadow of the lobby. Before the girl responded, her mother said sharply.

"Who is this you have brought with you at this hour." Her young sister was the only one to make a positive statement. "Oh Mary it is great to see you, give me a cuddle." During this time the brothers stood bemused and diffident. But her father was different. She knew the look of old; the brows down, and the stern face told its own story. He was not pleased. She went forward to kiss him and he welcomed, but his reaction was cool. "Who is this you have brought home tonight? Before she got any further the young man stepped forward. "My name is John, and I have come to ask your permission marry Mary. We felt you would want to look over your future son-in-law. I love her and want to marry her as soon as possible."

His entrance had been unexpected and resented; his challenge was like a clap of thunder stunning all to silence.

The air was tense. Once again the younger girl scaled the barriers. What a crowd; where will we all sleep? Mary can sleep with me" Addressing her brothers she informed them "You are all right you have your own bed. John can have the wee spare room up in the attic. We must get the bed clothes aired down at the fire."

Before anyone had the opportunity to say anything father butted in;;
"There will be no bed till something's are straightened out." Mother was quick to seize the opportunity. "That can wait. Let us get our supper; set two other places for Mary and John. They must be tired after the long journey from Oban."

The air thawed a little at this, and Robert and his wife rose and drew in chairs for the visitors but the atmosphere remained strained; the stranger seemed to be less put out than the rest, and coaxed the conversation along ordinary and well known lines.

Mary was more angry than embarrassed as she looked across at her father. He would never accept this situation; his Scottish pride condone the suggestion of marriage, and after all she was just nineteen. These thoughts and this affair rankled in her mind. Was this the father she adored? She remembered the words of her mother. "Her father could not get out of the house but she was at his heels."

It was an uncomfortable meal, and the boys were glad to call it a day "Off to bed folks; see you in the morning" was their goodnight.

Again mother was first to speak. "Margaret; bed for you as well, or you will never get up for the kirk. Mind tomorrow is Sunday, Mary and I will clear up the supper dishes." This they proceeded to do. It was a pair of stubborn men who were left to get on with their discussion, because it was evident things would have to be settled.

The man of the house was not at ease, but quickly brought the subject of this guest's intentions. Were his honourable? What were his prospects? What was his background? He sat with his brow furrowed and his face had a dour look as John answered. "Mr. McEachren I love Mary; have done since I got to know her on the croft next to mine I'm an Irishman born of Irish parents. I am not responsible for that neither am I shamed of it. I'm proud of my father and mother. They chose to come to Scotland; there was really no choice. The potato famine, and the starvation and iniquitous landlords at the government's command, forced the removal of thousands just as it happened in your own land. They have settled along the Solway Firth. They have lived there ever since...When I left school work was

126

scarce especially for 'tattie howkers' from Ireland. I left and made my way north and finally stayed in the job I have now... I can work and will be able to support her. There is a tied cottage where I live; it would go with the job."

He was interrupted "You seem to have everything planned. Does she know all this" Nodding in the direction of the kitchen.
"Ask her to come through and she will answer for herself.".

Meantime behind the shut door mother and daughter were having women's talk. "Do you love him lass? Will he be good to you? Mind you he is Irish and they don't get a very good name in this area."
"Oh mother; he is the man for me. He is gentle and kind although he looks big and strong."
"Listen Mary are you in the family way." Indignantly she replied;
"John is not like that. He would never take advantage of me, don't worry about us."

With that she had to be content. They went to join the men who were sitting at opposite sides of the fire. At their entrance talk between the men faded into nothingness.

Grudgingly the old man grunted
"You better get the bed made up for the young man. It is time we were all in bed."

It was the first time she and her boyfriend had slept under the same roof. Still it was a glorious feeling to slip outside for a few minutes to say their goodnights under the stars. So it was a subdued family that went to bed that night.
The boys got off to sleep without much trouble.

"Lassie's are only a plague, but he is no catch", was their light dismissal of the whole affair but the older folks with time to talk it over, did not do that. He refused to be mollified but he also refused to discuss it. Mother was cross with this old man of hers. She knew him of old. If once he saw reason in the situation he would relent and Mary would be back in favour. So sleep did not come easily to the wife and mother as she grappled with the unexpected news.

Morning finally dawned with a beautiful Sabbath sunrise. Regular jobs had to be done before time for the kirk, so breakfast was hurried. As they took their porridge she sensed an easing of the tension. She was glad of that; she did not like strain or dissension of any kind.

Margaret helped greatly and chatted her way through the meal, mostly questioning Mary about the wedding plans, and her part in it, but including everyone in the range of the conversation. Again John stepped into the breach as the talk wilted at the mention of the kirk.

"I may be Irish but we have been known to go to kirk. Where I lived on the Solway I went every Sunday. At that father's brow seemed less drawn, and he less thrawn, and he ventured the information that he was pleased to hear it.

It was an idyllic day, and it was he who issued his invitation or command "You three women take the trap; the laddies and I will walk. There is not room in the trap for us all."

With some misgivings John agreed, not wanting to cause anymore waves on the troubled waters. But the morning air must have had a beneficial effect on David McEachren for he talked away quite affably, about farm affairs in an informative way to an interested audience.

Something caught the attention of the brothers and they halted. This left the prospective son-in-law to make the best of it. John was sorry; what would this old carmudgen have to talk about, although only one subject occupied both minds. So they walked on in silence for a short distance. This silence was broken

"Son I am not against you; as far as I can see you are a decent enough young man, but I've only known you since yesterday. Another thing that worries me is the fact that you are twenty six and she is only a lass. By the way your Gaelic is not very good but I will not hold that against you."

This seemed to lighten the atmosphere. It certainly brightened the suitors "All I can say is what I said last night. She is the only girl I've courted I love her and will take care of her. You need have no fear of that."

Mary's father put out his hand and grasped John's "Thanks for these words lad, but if ever you let her down I'll be after you with a shotgun."

In the trap the conversation was about a mother losing her eldest to a man she did not know, and worse than that, she was going to live well away from home. In this the minister's sermon did not help. It concerned the story of the prodigal son. But the journey back was a lift to everybody when David declared "it looks like a shower of rain we'll all crowd into the trap." "They did that so it was a marvellous ride especially for the young lovers squeezed close together without any questions being asked. Were they not nearly all family? This was consolidated when the old man said in a lighter tone, than they had heard "Well mother you seem to be getting an addition to your family; a son-in-law. Does that not make you feel an old woman?" Quickly she retorted "Not half so old as last night. It is not what you say but how you say it that worries me. Other people do not know you as I; You don't even need to speak; one look at your face tells whither you are pleased or huffed.

So it was home for a celebration dinner. The best china from the top shelf made a grand array in the simple feast in a humble home.

There were tears kisses and hugs as well as handshakes the next morning. Jobs had to be accomplished before there was any gallivanting. The doleful air was lightened again with the intervention of Margaret.

"We all went together yesterday we can do the same today." At last they were aboard the boat; alone in the middle of a jostling crowd their love spilled over as they planned their future, and talked about the weekend and its outcome. "We will be married on the island..Your folks said it would be sensible to wait a year."
"I do not want to wait so long, I have been saving; it is not much but it will help." "I have some money saved; you know how much. We will stop in my present place until we find a wee place for ourselves. We will both be earning which will make up for the pittance you got from these miserable relatives of yours."

So they discussed plans for the future but it was not long till John's patience began to wilt and he said. "We have waited long enough. Soon they managed to get away to the island for an overnight. A surprise awaited them "When will we cry the banns; we knew you would not wait a year. We will see the minister."

They were married in the village church, and Margaret had her wish fulfilled. She was a beautiful bridesmaid, both at the wedding and the tea in the home, which was attended by most of the people around the district. The first night was spent in

130

the home; Margaret being banished temporarily to the wee room up in the attic.

The next morning was to see another tearful parting. Mary saw the sunshine and her beloved folks, through a mist of tears. When would she be back again? As it turned out it was to be a long time before she stepped ashore on the beautiful island again.

Marriage proved to be what it always was; not all kisses and cuddles but hard work. But after the first year they felt they had enough saved to enable them to buy a place of their own. They heard of one but it was away down in the industrial belt of Scotland. This proved another time of heart searching and big decisions had to be made. They had to depend on reports and advice of strangers, although some information had come from John's parents.

The fact that finally convinced them, was the arrival of a pony and trap a gift from her home with a note. This will be handy if you ever want to move. Both the young pony and the trap were in excellent condition and once Mary felt at ease with the move, she was more enthusiastic than he, and soon they were on the move.

It was a Scots spring morning; heavy clouds gathered over the north and west. Mary remarked "They are worse than the frown on my father's face, when I took you home for the first time, and be sure of this it will not be brightened by this latest move by that daft Irishman."

The weather seemed to agree for it poured with rain all the first part of their journey with a vengeance of anger at their betrayal. The mood in the trap under the coats and sacks was low as well John was the first to put his feelings into words "Do you think we are doing the right thing? Doubt creeping into his mind filled him with foreboding and fear. He had not just himself to please. There was this lassie whom he loved with all his heart, prepared to back him, and this made the responsibility all the heavier to bear. She broke his silence "I am not a wee bairn; I am a women in love with a big strong man. Maybe we should be glad to see the back of this land and it's weather. You have said often there are more wet days than dry."

As usual when the die is cast women are stronger than men, although the quieter. Her attitude was to be the compelling feature as they journeyed on in the rain. Nearing their stop for the night the weather dramatically changed and the evening was full of promise of a good day on the morrow.

They managed to find a small inn that could give them shelter for themselves, and stabling for the pony. The inn was full of travellers going north, and the conversation turned to prospects in the south. The response was quick and intriguing. It was a real promised land to which they were directed.

"Why then are you leaving?" "We are going home to the farm in Perthshire; my parents are past farming so we have to go back." Said the other man. "It is a good distance yet to the place you're going. But the farm is not good. It has been run down and will take a lot of money to build it up again. It is just near a mining village. I gave up farm work for the pits. The work is very different, but the shifts are shorter. You will have no trouble getting a house. There are always plenty of vacant ones. You should try it."

While getting ready for bed and indeed for an hour or two afterwards they weighed the pros and cons. Finally they made up their minds. They would go as far as this village before making any hasty decisions.

They planned their arrival for the forenoon of two days later, and stopped at a farm to ask for directions. The farmer and his wife were kindness itself when the story was told. The lady was quick to respond seeing the condition of this wee Lass. "You look as if you could do with your bed so I think it would be best if you stayed here for the night." So after a hearty meal it was bed for the overnight visitors.

The next day dawned clear and bright. When it was explained what the plans were, the farmer was upset.

"Do you mean to say you are going to be a collier? You better think about it; it is a tough and dangerous job and the people are not folks I would like to live with. By all the reports from farmers near the place they are a scruffy crowd. There are no gardens, but of course you do not need a garden if there are fields with potatoes and turnips beside the rows." His wife cut in on the conversation. Addressing the girl she said; "They are the roughest, coarsest women you could meet, and many are dirty into the bargain. You say you speak both English and Gaelic; that crowd don't speak either. Their language is as course as their manner. You would be better off with a job and house with some of the farms in this part. We will see that you get something around here more suitable, than what you have in front of you, if you feel that you cannot settle."

"Thank you; we will keep that in mind if we find we cannot manage." So it was on the road again and soon they were toiling up a steep hill then down past the school with its noise and laughter. The next landmark was the church with its attendant manse. This gave a boost to their flagging spirits. Surely this was the place to be; a school for the wee one that was coming and a church for Sunday School for all the children in the village it must be better than a highland glen with few young people.

They dreamed and made plans, but the main part of the village lay further on. They came to the square and drew up at the door of the inn. The Innkeeper was quick to spy the newcomers and was at the door in a hurry.

"Kin ah help yi" was his friendly greeting "Jist call me Hughie." As he invited them in for refreshment.

They told their story. The man was quick to assure them. "Ah ken the best place tae ask. The man that collects the rents steys along that row the saicind door fae the en. He'll fit yi up wae a hoose and tell yi aboot a joab. He kens aathin that goes on here"

They rode along the street. As they did so Mary pulled at her husband's sleeve. "All the women are at their doors." He replied "Those who are not at the door are looking from behind the curtains. You will not have any secrets."

They knocked as directed, but need not have bothered. The woman was quicker than they. Her salutation was quite abrupt but not unfriendly.
"Whit kin ah dae for yi" After they had explained their errand they were told that her Jimmy would fix them with a house. Whither Jimmy had been having a nap, or doing his rent business they were not sure, but soon he was at the door inviting them into the house.

"Your powny and trap will be aaricht. The schule isnae oot yit so there will be nae weans to bother it. Ah hiv goat the place for you; Ah'll show it to you as we gang along. The hoose bein at the end o' the row his a wee shed built on tae the en'; fine fur a horse. But whit are yi'gaun tae dae wi'a powny and trap if yi are gaun tae be a collier"?

134

"I do not know, but I would like to take you up on your offer. Could we see it?" It consisted of one room (a single end) with one window looking on to the street. Another family lived through the wall with their door and window opening on to the other road.

Mary was aghast. The room was empty and devoid of floor covering and curtains while walls had not seen paper for a long time. To add to her misery she saw a grate that had not known a fire for as long. On expressing her dismay she was assured by her guide that there was nothing wrong in it, that a pickle black lead and emery papers would not remedy. Certainly it would take time and elbow grease to accomplish this. The walls would need to be washed down and a coat of whitewash applied. The floor too, would need the same hard work, but a good scrubbing brush and carbolic soap was all that was needed to make it like new.

All these repeated assurances increased rather than lessened Mary's distress. John and she were not going to stay here. She was not afraid of hard work. There had been plenty of heavy jobs on the croft; was it not a way of life up there, but this was different. Who could put a place like this right? Her spirits were further lowered when she heard John saying "I think we should give it a chance. I will do the heavy work I know you should not be doing anything strenuous." But she could not be comforted and it was a very unhappy girl that ran to the haven of his arms to weep out her feelings.

The woman and her husband's talk did not help "I hardly know a word they say. The guide noted her distress and quietly suggested they should take time to think it over. They would wait outside. This left them alone to discuss.

Mary was angry, but her sobs won the battle. She had promised to love and obey this big man, so there was nothing she could do about the situation but accept the decision. Before she had regained some measure of composure Mrs Goodson came back into the room. "Listen lass ah ken yir upset and yir nicht it is an aafi'mess, but h've been speaking to Meg Rawlinson next door. She waants yi tae come in and see her hoose. Maybe that will make yi chinge yir mind"

They all trooped next door, It was not a far distance; you stepped from one step to the other. What a transformation. It was quite sparsely furnished, but everything was neat and tidy. There was a warm glow from the grate, and the blacks bits as well as the steel shone with a lustre that caught the eye. The brass fender along the front of the fire showed evidence of the same diligence and care. Bright curtains covering the window, were of good lace, and overall there was an air of cleanliness, that contradicted the hovel next door.

This took Mary by surprise; so much so there was a stirring of hope. This middle aged woman could manage to make this home beautiful. She would take on the challenge, and gradually knew she and John could do the same.

A movement reminded her that in the next two months any tasks for her would need to be light ones. She was further helped in her decision when the hostess exclaimed "The kettle's on the bile. You and yir man can wait and have a cup with us."

After half an hours chat John went to bring in the few utensils, clothing and bedding from the cart.

He decided to put his pony into the shed if it was fit for an animal. To his amazement the stable was in better condition than the house. There was plenty of straw in the corner, and it was fresh enough.

136

Having done this he went along to see Mr Baird the gaffer at the pit about a job. When he explained to the mining man his complete ignorance of pit work, he was told it would be a surface job, until he got used to the type of work that was done in pits. John was a bit worried; It was not as much money as he had expected but still it was more than he had earned on the farm. The rent man had said the rent was four and sixpence a week. At this stage he did not have many options, so he agreed to be at the pit on the Monday morning at seven o'clock.

The rest of this week would be required to get the house into order; work that he had at one time would have scorned. He buckled down with zeal and energy. He did find out that hard work accomplished great feats, but this first day was interrupted as he went to open the window to let in some air to the stuffy room.

The school had just released its prisoners for the day, from the bondage of the classroom to the freedom of the roads and rows. They still had time to stop at the house - old Geordie's "Mind him that deid last year - They're somebody flitted in ; yi' kin see in the windae noo. Let's shout in and run away roon the coarner."

They had the fright of their lives when stealthily they approached. The newcomer had heard the shouts of the boys as they came along the row, kicking a ball. The sudden hush made John go to the window. He gave a roar and it was to see who was first out of reach of this big wild man. It took some time before they ventured near again.

Two girls had enjoyed the spectacle and after they had hushed their laughter they decided to knock the door John and Mary received their new guests, and made then welcome. Work had to stop till all the questions on both sides were answered.

When the girls left, it was on the understanding that they would fetch the water from the well as well as go the messages. It had another reward. Round the rows the news was rapidly carried. "There is new folk in No.12 Lorn Street.

All the women had to see and size up the new folk. This was done by a nonchalant walk along the row to look in the window - jist in passing - not nosey. What a thing to say. There are some main forritsome whae knocked the door and shouted in a welcome or a query. One was heard to say "He's Irish yi'ken by the tonque o'him. My but he's a big chap, but she's only a wee smout; she is pitting oan a bit o'wecht Ah wunner when she's due?

John and Mary were overwhelmed by their reception; he thinking they are an inquisitive crowd and she taking the opposite view. They are only being kind to new people, but it certainly is a change from up north. If any one moved a few would help, but in the main you were on your own.

At the back of this new development, help was at hand with an old chair and two rag rugs-not too clean, but accompanying these gifts the information that if she needed it they would give her the graith, and show her how to make them. It was a great joab on a winter's nicht efter the new fire is bleezing up the lum. There were too many faces for Mary to put names to them all, but she was sure that would come in time.

John remained morose and quiet during this invasion of their privacy; saying he would not be happy if this went on every day. Before the night was through he was glad of the first day. They were strangers yet seemed to be accepted by this peculiar company of women. As he looked round the room at the end of their first day in this foreign land he was forced to admit that it took some doing to accept the manners, but their

138

kindness made up for that. Bed was a makeshift affair, but the bolster they had brought with them was cosy and warm with their own home spun blankets on top.

There was little respite for the big man from then on till Monday; not even a visit to the church, although there had been plenty of invitations to come along to Dunn's pub. He declined for two reasons; he had too much to do at home, and was not a drinker. When he expressed this there were queer looks directed his way.

"A hieland Irishman that disnae drink. What kin aman are yi. You go to the kirk as weel' whit dae ye dae wi' yir time?. John had no difficulty in finding some thing to take up his time as he looked around this place where he had brought his wife. Doubt stronger than ever surged through his mind - he thought of the work still to be done, and he was not contemplating Monday morning with any relish.

Monday did come and with it a completely new experience. The weather had changed and heavy clouds were pouring their contents down on this now dreary village, but he was far up on the top of the bing emptying hutches of dirt.. he was to learn quickly that a single old coat was not sufficient to keep you dry. Long before piece time he was soaked to the skin. He had been used to working in all kinds of weather, but after a few weeks he decided he would be better off down the pit. The money was better and it could not be as miserable as this. Any how the shift was shorter.

Another request to the gaffer was granted in the famous words "Stert on Monday morning, and dinnae be late or yi'll no get doon."...it was an experience he was never likely to forget, and had less notion of repeating, but he was back the next day and for a further year. He hated every minute on the job from the first day. It was hard and it was cramped. It certainly was not so windy; there was very little rain at all, and what there was, did not seem fresh and clear as the summer mornings on the croft. The more he thought of his home in the highlands, the more he determined to get out of this hole.

The place where he was sent was a hard place, men said. Before the day was out he understood what that meant. The old man, irascible, and crabbit, was not inclined to give the young man much assistance at his job of filling and pushing full hutches out a road where you could not skin a cat. He would have swopped with any of the men on the top of the bing whatever the weather. Before finishing time his arms and back were scarred by the low roof and the tight roadway and his legs could hardly carry him out to the pitbottom. He learned something; the bigger you are, the less room there is in these little roads.

He had longed for home, not in a miner's row, but back in the freedom of his country glen. He had thought of Mary; trying to make a home out of a hovel. His first concern on entering the house at the end of the shift "How are you lass? You are doing far too much and I'm worried about you."

She in turn was not happy either, as he told her of his day in the dark. She would never get reconciled to her man doing such dangerous and dirty work. A wee lamp like the one he used would not provide any real light; had he not tried it this morning before he left the room, and it hardly touched the walls of this wee place.

They settled down, and both began to take a real pride in their little home, it took the semblance of order and cleanliness as they gathered some odds and ends of furniture. The brass fender that John had bought from a workmate was now as

140

sparkling as the one that had made such an impression on them. It was a constant reminder of their despair, and the following experience of seeing a daily improvement.

The arrival of her first born son, and the care for him was a dreadful ordeal. The doctor had come, and after examination pronounced there was no need for him to come back, unless there were complications. Jenny the midwife was first class at her work, and he had very confidence in her. The wee woman was to prove a mother as well as a midwife and so started a friendship that lasted for years, and was the main reason for them settling in and becoming part of the community.

John was proud of his son and was not averse to enthusing about him to his mates at work "Wait tae yi've goat a dizzen about yir feet; yi'll no crow nae cruise." He soon learned to keep quiet about this wonderful son of his.

The novelty had long worn off, these seasoned miners, with every additional mouth to feed, an added obligation to keep the money coming in.

It was during this first year he had the idea he could put the pony and trap to good use. This sprung from an incident, when a neighbour required a conveyance to take him to see a relative in the next village who was ill. Gradually the news got round that big Jock the Irishman was not hard to pay, so this boosted the family funds.

He and Mary were determined not to fall into the error of most of the villagers. 'There was nothing you could do about your circumstances you just accepted things as they were and got on with living the only life you knew' They did prove their independence. This meant John taking time off his work occasionally to do his part time job, but this came to the attention of the manager who was not long in calling him into the office where he was warned of his attendance. There would be no more warnings, but the sack.

Fortunately they had felt for some time that with a bit of pinching and tightening of their belts, a living, although not lavish, would be possible. John had other things in mind. The coal for the village and surrounding farms and cottages was done by a man with a horse and cart. He was keeping his ear to the ground, for he knew that old Geordie the coal man was intending to give up before long, so with that in mind, he attended a roup at a nearby farm and saw an outfit that would suit his purpose; a sturdy cart horse with a decent cart to go with it. He had been astute enough to ascertain that the old horse was retiring with its master Geordie, so with the money saved he made his purchase. It was a proud man that rode back into the village on his own horse and cart.

With the idea of buying old Geordie out John approached him and was pleased to hear that the cash asked for was still within his budget. He was given the details of the loose contract with the pits which would give him a monopoly of this kind of cartage at a reasonable figure.

There was considerable resentment in the village to this. The women argued "Why should he get it." Was heard often along the rows. The reason for his success, was the age old fear of men to take a step out of the known into the unknown. The other men who could have done the work as well, had neither the confidence nor the money, to venture into this risky business.

John did not worry too much about the opinions of the old wives. He was Irish; different from them. He would succeed! This he commenced to do and before long he set himself up to transport flittings about the village and beyond and it became a well known fact that big Jock never took a flitting without scrubbing out his cart; no fear of getting things dirtied or wasted with him. Invariably this would be followed by the remark Mary Grayfield is as clean as he is; look at the kind o'hoose she keeps - spotless and her with two weans and another one due, she is nice and friendly as well. She does a lot for the kirk and her hoose is never empty. The weans are never kept at the door but oot and in like bees at a byke. This summing up might be interpreted that the family had finally been accepted.

It was a great sound on a winter's night to hear a knock at the door and find someone asking about the use of his horse and cart. "Ma faither waants yi tae tak a flitting up tae the tap of the brae."

All this time that expansion was going on, events at the single end had changed as well. With the increasing family Mary had complained about the lack of space and was constantly at the rent man about a bigger house. This caused some resentment among some of the neighbours, and this was expressed forcibly down at the Co "Where dis she think she is; getting up in the world. It's oor money she is spending" But even the most hostile had to admit "She's no stuck up but free wi everybody."

The years past. The girl was small and thin but the two growing laddies were the spitting image of their father. With the family growing up in this environment, it was little wonder that the soft tone of the highlands and the Gaelic, lost ground to the rough talk of the mining community. This was a distress to the mother in the home, who endeavoured to keep the old tongue alive.

With the increasing chores of her daily life and the insistent clamour of a growing family Mary finally confined the use of her favourite Gaelic to the times when she sang to each succeeding member of her growing brood, as she rocked the wooden cradle.

The latest baby arrived just when Michael was leaving school. He would be a miner like all the rest of the boys, he was not going to be a coal carter like his father. They would not shout after him as they did with his father "Mick the Irish Coalman" His pals were always getting on to him at school, Irish paddy they would call him. They did this for some time because, although, he had his father's build he had his mother's quieter nature.

This was to change dramatically one day in the playground. The biggest boy in the school, and also the worse bully, was up to his old tricks of causing misery to all and sundry. He kicked one of the smaller boys and Michael challenged him "Kick somebody your own size" He proceeded to do just that, and aimed a kick at Michael. Before it landed, he was surprised to see his opponent coming at him with raised fists.

The fight did not last long. The bully's supremacy soon withered under the onslaught and a final punch on his nose finished the contest. A bloody nose is the thing that usually ends a boy's fight. Never again would he rule the roost. If he ever did get out of hand with the young ones, all that was required was the jibe "Ah'll tell Micky on yi; He'll sort yi oot."

It took them years before they were fully settled for Mary had determined from the first day she had been faced the challenge. Would she stay, or head out for the well known and loved places from which she had come?

John had not involved himself with village affairs and always kept himself a bit aloof. His family and home were all that mattered to big John. Two boys and two girls, with his wee

144

wife constituted his world, and so it remained till they moved away as the village disappeared into history.

The elder son Michael married a local girl and was last to leave; they joined the family firm of haulage contraction. The other son never married; he was looking for a woman like his mother. You never find one and neither did he.

The two girls were not as hard to please and quickly found men like their father. Mother was heard to say on numerous occasions "That would be a hard job: I did not think there was another like him."

So we leave them as they start out on a new life in the anonimity of a large town where the neighbours did not pop in for a crack and a cup of tea.

CHAPTER 11

OCCUPATIONS IN THE VILLAGE.

Work for men was mainly in the pits, but before looking at that, a place must be found for the real heroines of the day. Women filled the role of wife, mother, accountant and slave to the whole family.

All water for cooking and the making of tea had to be boiled on an open coal fire with a swey or swee (a movable iron bar hung over a fire on which pots and kettles were hung. It had it's attendant swee chain.) It would be a rare thing to see a house without this apparatus, with a soup pot hanging, simmering over the fire, ready for the return of hungry men and boys from their work. It would also be needed to keep hot water for all the other household chores during the day. At dinner time other pots would be arranged round the hob in order of preference and need.

Few houses had a washing house, so that, too had to be catered for in the weekly routine of the home. In some few cases communal wash houses would be supplied for a certain number of houses. A number of homes would require its use so you took it in turns. You were allocated one day per week, and if you started with a Monday that was your slot for all time. Many nevertheless, were the rows, and fights as well, if someone broke the system.

146

The fire was the focal point in the kitchen; the nearer you could crush in, the warmer it was, so it was usually the older and stronger that acquired the best seats. The door opened right on to the road; those on the perimeter had little heat and the worst of the draughts from the ill fitting door.

It might be difficult to imagine the scene at lousing, when a father and two or three sons came home. They would be dirty with caked sweat and dust. Stour or perhaps moleskin trousers would be soaking wet and muddy. Fortunately there were no fitted carpets but waxcloth on the floor. This of course had to be washed after the ablutions were over. The bine, or the zinc bath, was drawn up near the fire, and father would wash first. The last to use the bath would not have very hygienic conditions for his dip. If this had to be carried on in a single end, chaos might be the descriptive term for the exercise.

It was always the women's job to clean up the mess and empty the bath water into the sheugh (sheugh-an open drain for dirty water.) After the place was put back to normal by placing the rag rugs in position, if there were any, it was time for dinner. You would see the reason for the swee and the heavy pots. Soup would be served every day with mostly boiling beef and tatties to follow; mince might make a welcome change but on wash days it might be a single course. One might ask the question. What about the dirty clothes? Simple; if they were wet they were hung around the fire to dry, and if dry, they were taken outside and brushed or beaten (dauded) against the side of the house, or beside the door, and left out to air, if weather was suitable. Boots were subject to the same treatment, but in most homes these would be cleaned and polished and left at the door to air.

In the morning there would be the task of putting on clothes that had been dried but not washed. Underwear consisted of a singlet and drawers (salmon pinks they were

147

called). These were home knitted with heavy wool. These were supplemented by a rough shirt and socks, you would lift your pit jacket from the back of the door as you left. The wee claith bunnet capped the lot. You were fully prepared to face the rigours of another shift, when you lifted your piecebox and tin flask, and shouted; "Ah'm away hen, see you at lousing time." This would be around five o'clock in the morning, while the children were still in the land of Nod.

Morning dayshift really centered around the head of the house. He could be up and away before the sons surfaced. He was lucky; the melee that followed would have made a good script for some comedian. If two or three sons were on the early shift as well, and clothes laid out to heat in front of the fire, many and varied would be the reactions when getting dressed.

To keep everything in context, this could all be done in a single end. Imagine copping with this every day. There were compensations: the wife got washing her man's back every day. Where there were a few sons of pit age in the family there might be a daughter or two harnessed to this treadmill. The more fortunate of the girls would be away to some town or domestic service, drudgery of a different kind, that was not much improvement.

Another task for the wife and mother was the making up of the piece for each man. This was often done the night before, and consisted of four slices of plain bread -pan loaf was not acceptable. "There wis nae fattening in it." The filling for these sandwiches never varied; Jam or cheese overlying a scrape of margarine or butter. The piece box was made of two tins; one fitting into the other with a flat end, and a rounded one, so that the slice would fit into the box. An oft repeated assertion from a frugal housewife. "Nae man or faimily o' mine is gaun tae the pit wae a piece made up the nicht before. Ah widnae hae the shame o'it."

148

So before the breakfast was made, the piece was made up with its accompanying flask of tea filled from a freshly brewed teapot. This was then wrapped in an old sock to keep it fairly warm till piece time. In some cases it would be a bottle of cold water.

Except in unusual circumstances, like giving birth to another wean, this was the general practice. Neither wonder they did not scratch an old (pow) head. After getting rid of the men it was time for the children to be roused for school. It was difficult enough to deal with taciturn and crabbit men; it was no easier with the children, apart from the fact, she yielded more authority. In addition to sorting out clothes and helping some of the smaller children to dress, the porridge pot had to have its attention. The school footwear would have been attended to, along with the pit boots or just before mother went to bed. Add a little mending; done in the spare time she had might constitute a rest. In the pride of her home the adage was heard by a diligent housewife 'There is shame in a hole but none in a patch.'

Depending on the distance from home to school children carried a piece or ran home at dinner time. Perhaps women would be glad to make up a piece or two in the morning, rather than have the bother of interruption in the middle of a busy day. Four o'clock was early enough for weans to be under your feet.

There would be time put your feet up and enjoy a cigarette and the daily paper; no! This would be a time for the knitting needles and a cup of tea, before preparation for the pit to release its workforce for the day.

The burden of keeping the Cooperative book clean, was obviously her province as well. Keeping a roof over your head, meant paying the rent whenever it was due. Over on the negative side was the fact that there was no health service. If the man was off ill, no money was coming into the house, except the poor relief fund - it was termed the Pairish. This was the ultimate of poverty. In the modern language it was 'means tested' rigorously.

Friendly Societies were to bring some help in this matter; this was a scheme whereby you paid weekly into this, and when you were off with a doctor's line you were paid out of the funds. Later when a government scheme was started for insurance benefit, the money that came from the previous source was a real windfall. It was 1910 before compensation was paid for injury at work.

Unemployment was something else to be dreaded; it was work or want, so in the case of the village in 1891 they were fortunate. Only one person is mentioned in that category. Married women rarely went out to work. Her herculean task at home would occupy all her waking hours. In another context, when work ran dry men and families were cast adrift and many were reduced to beggary.

Given these circumstances there was a financial reason for starting work before you were completely healed or cured. Many have been the cases where this was true, and in the longer term benefited neither company or collier. Doctors then, were not in the habit of handing out sicklines or compensation ones just for fun, so monetary conditions in the home, and the fear of debt drove them back to work.

One example of this; a young man working on the pit top was pulling a tub on to the cage. This usually was a simple operation. When the cage came to the surface he put his hand over the top of the tub to pull it on to the cage. As he did so, another tub would come round to take its place. On this occasion he followed the correct procedure, but unfortunately there were no buffers on either of the tubs and his hand was caught between them as they crashed together. He lost the tip of his small finger, as well as bursting it further down. The next finger was badly crushed and the nail torn away. In this case human flesh and bone were not substantial enough to prevent the accident. It was post haste to the doctor's surgery for attention.

After two weeks off his work he had a letter from the compensation office calling him to present himself for examination in Glasgow. There, he was commanded to take off the bandages. They examined his hand and told him to put them back on again, with his left hand and his teeth to tie the knots. During this struggle there was a discussion between the three doctors.

The verdict; he was offered two weeks money if he would sign off. The boy had been told by his father not to sign off, as this would be the end of his compensation; not only so, but it would clear the company of any need to pay, no matter how long he was off work. Even if he started again and had to lie off, because he could not manage the job, there would be no further payment. He went back to work after three weeks idle time.

This case did not happen away back in the last century; it took place in 1935 in a colliery owned by a large coal company. Great strides had been made? Liability was in operation by the time of the last incident but was extremely difficult to pursue. Cases like this were legion.

While it was to be condemned the other side must be mentioned. One man who exploited the system, had signed on the Insurance and had received a doctor's certificate and never worked for years, living on the benefits and his parish money. He supplemented his income with handouts from kindly church groups.

A new doctor was appointed, and while going through his notes, decided to call in some long term cases for review. He was on the list and was promptly told to get a job; there was nothing wrong with him. He went back to work, and never lost a shift for years, till retiring. He worked seven days a week, and never went to his church again.

The same type of thing happened to men on unemployment benefit. Father and son went unemployed for years; indeed the father never worked again. Authority caught up with the younger member of the family when he was ordered back to work. He, too, went back to the pit and for the rest of his working life hardly ever missed a shift, as well as working extra shifts on overtime.

CHAPTER 12

SOURCES OF INCOME

Apart from the pits, employment for men was mainly confined to farm service with a few labouring jobs. As far as time spent on the job was concerned this had longer hours, with rarely any specified finishing time. The drawback was the fact, there was no early finish on the Saturday, while work carried over into Sunday with no extra money. In the pits work started an hour earlier than the rest of the week. This suited the football players and their supporters. It was also a night when you were free of the need to go to bed early, for an early start on the Sunday.

It was also a night for your feet on the sawdust. (This statement was coined from the fact that most shops and all pubs had sawdust spread on the floor.) There always seemed to be a gap between the two ways of earning a livelihood. You did not mix with the other side and for some unknown reason colliers looked down on the teuchters, as they termed farm labourers.

Some few shops did business in the village on a full time basis; e.g. Hugh Dunn's public house and provision store down in the square. Dominock O'Donnell, Wm Kechans, John Haughans and Mary Ann Nimmo. Of these, three of the shops were still trading into the 1920's. Kechans at Greenbank a haven for bona fide travellers kept going well into the Second

153

World War, Men who lived outside the three mile limit, which was kept, if it was not possible to break it. Local men could not drink at their own pub as usual, but perforce had to journey further afield.

Hugh Dunn's was a popular place for cronies to meet. Here the stories of the victories of the team would be analysed on a Saturday night. Along with the great catches of fish from the local burns and rivers, and the state of the nation. It was going to the dogs, even then by all accounts.

The coming of West Calder Cooperative Societey in 1894 severely cut into all their trade.

In addition there were three tailors; James Hamilton, Wm.Donaldson and his son. It is recorded that three dress makers plied this trade; Susan Ross and her daughter Maggie, as weel as Teeny Todd who lived at Harryfoothill.

There was also a shoemaker Pat Mulddon and a clockmaker while the manager of one of the collieries James Malcolm had a coachman-John Syme. Daniel Muir; a pedlar lived in the village, or he may have been staying for the day only.

By this time the railway had been opened from the main line at Auchengray to Wilsontown and collieries beyond, so the station master - John Paymor and his assistant, his son John. The doctor at this time was George Thomson M.D., Haywood Rows.

These seemed to be a wide range of surnames. This might be expected when the catchment area was so wide., but first names were more limited and common as each family followed the same pattern. No fancy names were expected or allowed. This was before the days of film stars and television personalities. There was a strict order: oldest son was called after his

154

paternal grandfather; the next after his maternal grandfather. The same system was sacrosanct with the girls. All succeeding sons and daughters were named after uncles and aunts of which there did not appear any scarcity.

This inevitably leads on to the thought of family units. Family planning was virtually unknown, and therefore seldom practised. No sex education but an acceptance of a situation which was akin to all the problems of the day, 'You grinned and bore it.'

Six in a home was the average; either in one room or two. These were termed single ends or double ends. The census of the year proves the above statement. While looking at statistics, this was indeed the true figure. While the average figure does not look too bad, a glance over the full details gives a sombre picture. One case at least is mentioned; husband and wife with eight children - the oldest twenty three and the youngest three. How did they find the space, yes and the energy? They were tough.

John Murray. His wife Secilia was born in Co.Sligo Ireland. One of the sons - Alex at thirteen years of age, along with Thomas Tennant and John Watson were the youngest mine workers in the census of 1891. This must rival the youngest farm worker in 1841 - Wm Bryce age twelve years old.

Another record seemed inevitable till your attention is turned to Thomas Ballantyne; farmer at Buchknowes, where there were ten in the family and three workers.. Space would be more plentiful on a farm. There were another seven families of ten members quoted.

Perhaps the first prize should got to George Burt, whose family of eleven had the luxury of two rooms. The story is told of the occasion when mother was out for the evening and father was responsible for putting the weans to bed. When mother arrived her first question, of course was to ask how had the children behaved? The reply from the man of the house. "They were nae boather tae it wus time fur bed and that yin in the middle wid not go to sleep. He finally fell over when I threatened to tell his mother when she came home."

The lady's reply was scathing. "Dae ye no ken yir ain weans? That's the laddie frae next door."

This brings back the nightmare of the attempts to keep up the pace. Women must have longed for the days when they were past child bearing age. In more modern times, when the village slums were being cleared out; the families moved to another village. Some of these new tenants were not received with any great degree of friendliness, and it was some time before some were accepted.

One outstanding example is worthy of note. One block of council houses-two stories high had four families allocated to this building. Each house had five rooms. Each home housed an average of thirteen making a grand total of fifty two.

This was utopia for all concerned. Hot and cold water from taps but the biggest miracle of all was the shining new bathrooms. No running around the back to the dry closets; with electric light both inside and outside. The modern times were 1931 or 32.

CHAPTER 13

A RESIDENT'S ACCEPTANCE

Meg Rawlinson tells her story.

My husband Charlie and I have lived in the village all our married lives. We came to this mining community in its infancy. We have lived in the same single end all these years. The good Lord never gave us children of our own, and this was a great regret to us both. What woman and man does not want weans about the house? Nevertheless we were content with our lot.

In our early fifties a young couple came to the house next door. Very trig they were; good clothes and clean and tidy. They came unexpectantly-no warning or hint that new neighbours were coming, and what an outfit to stop at the door; no less than a pony and trap. You did not see many of these about the rows. These were for the knabbery (gentry). I remember it was a sunny day.

The rent man and his wife were with them. It was they who brought them in to see my house. I think the young wife was so upset about the condition of the room she had been greiting gey sair. Mind you the place had stood empty for a good long time; it was an old widower who was the last tenant, so it was not spick and span.

My new visitor brightened up quite a bit when I suggested a cup of tea and a chair at the fire. I took to her right away and felt happy about the whole business. I hastened to assure her that she would have all the help she needed to get the place to rights.

I had early visions when I saw she was pregnant Oh; if a wee one comes next door, what a different it would make to Charlie and me. I had the weans running in and out of our house before they were born. I cannot say how eagerly I looked forward to my man's return from the pit to tell him my news. He would be as happy as a sandboy.

I told her not to worry after she said she had two months to go I would take her to the Doctor and arrange for Jenny the midwife to call in and see her. With that she went back next door.

There was no coal or sticks, but they had brought some pots and pans. They had a new kettle. After the introduction, I told John to go to our coal bunker at the front, and soon he had a blazing fire. It was not long before he and I were on our knees with hot water and a scrubbing brush each. The husband had washed down the walls with cold water, and a right mess he had made of it; at least the windows were clear of cobwebs.

Growing in my mind were doubts about my man's reaction to this new development. We had been so long without close neighbours, and any time that it had been talked about, he had always said "I hope it's a quiet couple like ourselves." They would not bother anybody.

I had the right to be anxious; Charlie was not pleased when I broke the news to him as he bathed in the bine (Tub) in front of the fire.
"Before long they'll be oot an in. We'll get nae peace in oor ain hoose." Before many months had passed, his gloomy forebodings were realised, and did he enjoy it.

He ruined everyone of the four weans. I told him repeatedly that he would have given them the clock off the wall to play with. As the days and weeks went by, I felt quite jealous of wife and weans. After all Mary was a lovely lass and he was only fifty. Talk about being fond of the bairns; he though the sun shone out of Mary's eyes. He laughed me to scorn and soon my fears were allayed; he was the same kind man I had married a long time ago.

That young couple put a lot of work into that single end. Mind you I don't think they were stuck for a shilling, and all the years we stayed together she was not mean or selfish; but she knew how to make the pay last. She was a credit to her folks up in the highlands of Scotland. She had this advantage her man did not drink; just on special occasions.

I was just being neighbourly, but soon that wee lass was as good as a daughter to me, and she treated me like another mother. She had a rough time at her confinement and she missed her mother. I think it was at this time that a special bond was formed between us, and I was able in some measure to help the doctor and Jenny.

I remember that first event as if it had been yesterday. I said a wee thing the minister had included in his Christmas season. "A woman forgets her travail in the joy that a man is born into the world."

I thought of the homes like my own, who were denied this honour and privilege; also homes where there seemed to be an endless train of ones, and not enough to feed them. Charlie and I had been thrifty all our lives. We could have had room in our hearts and homes for two or three wee weans.

Suppose I say it myself; I helped her to settle in, and introduced her to some of the neighbours I knew them all and proceeded to give her the low-down on some of them. "Hae nae truck wi them. Ah ken them weel hae nothing to do with them." Her answer was quick and to the point. "I think Mrs Rawlinson it would be better if I made up my own mind." I'll say this about Mary; and it says a lot for her.She could speak her mind when it was made up.

Going back to that first day.
I listened while my man moaned, but after dinner he consented to go next door, with this admonishment. "Ah'm scrubbing nae flairs or pooin paper off the wa." So we went next door; Charlie himself is nae wee smout (small and insignificant) but alongside John he was dwarfed.

Between them they soon had a makeshift bed made near the fire. The lass certainly looked as if she needed it.

While the two men went to get some sticks of furniture round at the old pedlar chap; he kept a simple and meagre supply of household goods. I got her into bed. She seemed desperate to get out of her clothes before the men returned.

She got a lick and a promise; a wee dicht tae the morning. I had quite a struggle fighting for her in the village; some folks do not like anybody better than themselves, although in most of these cases they have only put themselves there. I was never far away when help was needed. I was quite immune to the coarse comments of some of the women. "Yi wid think she wis a clucking hen they wey she treats that lassie."

The Co, or the store, as we call it, was situated down beside the railway line, I took her down to join the Co and get her book. There was a number of women that morning; aye some who would be better tidying the house instead of miscalling the neighbours. This morning there were some jibes about Irish and Hieland folk that should have stayed away frae oor village. I will tell you; I did not miss them, and hit the wall. I was angry at the treatment. It was another time that Mary showed her mettle. "It is all right Meg; they will get to accept John and me, for we have no intention of being quarrelsome." This did not satisfy me. I determined to hae the last word. "The herts the pairt aye that makes us richt or wrang." But no; in comes big Jean with the bigger mouth. She had her contribution to make, as well. "Ma man wis tellin me that he heard that Jock wis tryin to keep in wi auld Georgie-yi ken him that's gien up his coal run. It'll be a shame if he gets it." I was determined to get my pennyworth in as well. "Your man does not know the back end of a horse from the front, so what are you greiting about." I think that morning was the turning point in Mary's relations with the folk of the village. In fact I was too busy to listen to the clavers (Gossip). Aye and less patience.

Charlie and I had had our life fulfilled when wee Michael came. Our joy was complete in the bringing up of the other three as well as the first. The only thing at which Charlie rebelled, was my suggestion one night, that he should take a turn down the row with the wean in the shawl.

"Na na lass, folk are talking aboot me and the bairn. Whit kind o'life wid ah hae when ah went doon in the first tow the morn's morning. I wid never leeve it doon. Forbye that; his ain faither wid not do it."

This was a favourite way of getting around with infants, but it was strictly women's work. Mind you I heard of two men talking of their early days and one said to the other who was a member of a large family
"I never saw your father out without a wean in the shawl." The answer was pointed and definite "Wae had mair right tae cairrie them; whae wis to blame for them being there?"

Charlie never missed a night without going in to see the new arrival. His usual question after the dinner was past was, "Are ye gaun in tae see the wean it'll be near his bedtime. Maybe Mary will let me haud him and heat his wee feet at the fire."

I would not hear of this every night and laid down the law " I'm not and neither are you. Give the folk peace in their own home; I do declare that John sees less of the child than you."

Charlie had a backer in Mary. At first it had been Mr Rawlinson but I got that rectified with Mary.
"You would not let me say Mr to your man so Charlie will be as proud as a peacock if you call him by his first name."

I found to my joy that life had taken on a new outlook. Before this we had drifted along, preparing for old age. I was now a granny in my own mind although the other grannies were related. I wonder if they resented me for this great privilege. I talked to Mary about a visit to her parents. She was happy I asked, but expressed a doubt about John. "John will be no bother. I'll make up for your absence. I will be in my element-two men to look after."

Mary was only away for a week. Company at dinner time was a change; two men to talk of their day in the pit. He always washed at home but I tidied up behind him while the men blethered over the fire. We saw a lot of him that week; he was like a knotless thread. If every a man on his own was hapless he was that man.

Mary was looking the better of her holiday, and soon young John was toddling behind Michael, who, on occasions, was a bit rough with his wee brother.

This was the time when Charlie's prophecies prove true.

162

My door was never shut to these two boys. This did not prohibit Mary from lecturing her husband about Charlie's softness. She would need to be like me to draw the line. He was not as young as he was so he must take it easy. It was a blessing there were women to keep a happy balance. I do not know how these weans would have grown up. But the soft touch was much in evidence with us as well.

In John and Mary's little end...which was filling up with possession and the presence of youngsters, all were feeling the squeeze. John had been trying for some time to get a bigger house but it was a year before he heard about a suitable one. It was a double cottage rented by two families. By this time Mary had arrived and as she grew the boys slept with us. We had bought a small bed with the view to giving them a shot in granda and gra n's house for the night, every so often. This was different. Scampering feet heralded their approach every night.

Fortunately this did not last too long, for quite unexpectantly John came home with the news. He had called at a house with coal and the lady had asked him in for a cup of tea. While drinking this he was told that the family were leaving to go to another mining area, where prospects were better. He told them he was interested, she gave him all the information and sat down and wrote a letter to the proprietor. He could take a run into Lanark and fix it up. He was the first to know about the move, so he should get the best chance.

It was a delighted Mary who digested the news-two rooms and a kitchen. Later doubts crept in again. What about Meg and Charlie? We had bonded together these few years, and we would miss them. The weans, Michael, David and wee lass would miss next door with its cosy environment, so pleasant and homely.

I assured them that we would not forget them-it was not a hundred miles away. The only inconvenience; the stable for the pony and the cart horse would need to stay till one was built nearer the new house.

The person who deserved most sympathy was Charlie; he went about with a face that would trip him. He was not slow to side with the two boys-no need to flit-we were managing fine. I had to be quite firm with him and tell him "What can't be bettered maun be tholed" My own life would seem empty without my young friends, and I did not want to lapse into the way of life I had left so far behind. Midday tea would be a problem; I could walk over in ten minutes and of course Mary could bring the wee one in the shawl. The boys could come in from school in the middle of the day for their tea, before rushing back to the playground for the football so they would see quite a bit of me.

The boys would miss Charlie. He would not get along to see them every night, as had been his custom. When they complained I tried to tell them that he was getting to be an old man and his work at the coalface was very hard. This did not satisfy them; granda the third was not old; he always was ready to play with them. He was not like old Billy who walked with two sticks, or look at old Jimmy Waterson; he couldn't walk the length of the row without stopping twice for a rest. Then see old Bella; all she could do was sit at the door in the sun happit with shawls.

These really were old people but not granda. He walked the fields and hedge rows looking for birds nests; he was a champion at finding them in the queerest places. Did he not carry their wee sister when she got tired.. Logic is not a thing that occupies the minds of energetic boys, who see a great pastime and friendship come to an end.

164

I could hardly blame the children; I was not looking forward to the move any more than the next. There would be no excuse to run round if I heard the infant crying. I would miss the delight of carrying her in the shawl down the rows showing her off to envious neighbours. "She's as proud as a peacock." Another whispering "She is like a dug wi two tails." And another "She looks younger every day." So the two familes settled dowm to wait the news from Lanark but the news came through at last. Would Mr.Grayfield call at the office at his earliest convenience. The present occupants had given a month's notice and had supplied the firm with his name as a prospective tenant. It was summer and John was quick to take up the opportunity to arrange for a day out for Mary and me to go with him.

"We'll take the pony and trap and have a picnic on the road. When did you last have a day away from home Meg." You'll get holding the wean all the road if you, like Charlie and the laddies can fetch for themselves that day.

It was true what John said. I did not get away very often. Everything worked out as planned-a dry day with the picnic baskets first stop the Through-burn to sit beside the burn, then after the meal to lie back in the fresh grass for a rest.

I had been a bit sceptical about the long journey, but I was amazed how much I was enjoying the outing.

On our arrival we were all ushered into a sort of writing room and John was asked to wait and the gentleman would see him as soon as possible. Soon he was called in, and he was in for quite a time. We were beginning to wonder if there had been a slip up and he was not getting the house, when the door opened and John came out. His words were a bombshell to me "Meg' the gentleman would like to speak to you. I'll come back in with you." He did and I was glad; I had never been in an office in my life.

"Take a chair Mrs Rawlinson," and after I heard the news again I was glad I did. "Your friend has explained about your friendship over the years and how blest they are with folks like you and your husband next door. How would you like to move next door to them again. Mind you the rent is a good bit higher. Do you think you could manage it" quoting the rent.

"My man and I will never be back with the rent." I didn't tell him, but I would have been prepared to pay a bit more than the rent offered.

"You will hae to pay a month in advance but I will let you send on the money."

I did not have that kind of money on me but John soon remedied that.
"I will square the bill for the lady." Said he, and I could have kissed him.

What a day this was turning out to be. Wait till Charlie hears this; he will want to flit the morn. If I was enjoying the day up to this point I was now in heaven. I could not get home quick enough to see my man's face when I gave him the news.

So the association was back on its old footing; next door to each other. How I blessed the day when this wee lass, and her man chapped on my door. From being private persons reserved in the display of affection for old and young we were now part of a family. From solitary lives, John and I had come to share a relationship where love and caring provided the happiness of belonging.

As the years passed, I made friends with more people. There are worse personalities than being an adopted granny out in the fresh morning with a wee one in the shawl. He was a link that forged for me, friendships that lasted all my time.

166

I will remember that jaunt to Lanark and the sudden events made my cup feel as if it could take no more; but I was wrong. We stopped for a rest and a bite where we had picnicked in the morning. John had taken the bairn up the burn to see the fish when Mary imparted the news. "I am expecting again. You should have seen John's face when I told him: you could not ruin this one anymore than you did with the rest." I told him.

I agreed "He is a big burlyman but he's nothing but a big soft lump, as far as these weans are concerned. He's worse than Charlie and that's saying something." I have always tried to speak proper with Mary to keep her from getting into the way of speaking like us.

The next few years were happy ones; the family mixing with the villagers. It was a home where folks were made welcome; it became a haven for young laddies an lassies where games were played and special parties were held. We knew the benefit as well, and were involved in many of the games. Our house was in demand when anyone was staying over night; no, not for the visitors, but for the two young men or the two beautiful daughters of the house. It seemed to be a refuge if any of them were feeling hard done by as well.

Special young men and women were seen more often next door on the slightest pretext.

Sadly these days had to end. Word was filtering through of trouble at the local pits; the last section was being worked in No.9 and water in No.4 was a big problem. There will soon be no pits left. Everybody will need to move or take the workmen's train to the two big pits. When this happens the village is finished.

Meg's words were proved to be true. The inhabitants had to move far and near; The young to carry on the mining

167

tradition, and the old to talk of roads brushed and stents stripped, along side the gruesome story of these hated coal owners, and in all the telling, the feats of miners improved with the telling.

CHAPTER 14

AUCHENGRAY AND WULLIE WOODCOCK

Auchengray - Census 1851 and 1891

In the census of 1851 the village is noted to have sixty four inhabitants; this includes two farms in the village. The other farms outwith the village are not mentioned.

Of this number thirty six were born inside the Parish of Carnwath. Twenty eight were born in an area mainly surrounding, and not too far away from their new work and residences. It had robbed the populace: not as the far away places, as in the case of Haywood, where migration occurred from Inverness, Lairg, Skye Islay, Dumfries and Ireland.

Mention is made of two from across the water-Catherine Kirk and John Elliot, with a visitor. In the main its catchment area comprised the town of Carstairs, Liberton, Lanark, Kirknewton, West Calder, Kirkliston and Ratho: Douglas, Peebles and Leadhills were the boundaries.

It is of interest that the head of the family is quoted, in many instances as being born outwith the Parish; at least, some are mentioned.

George Ballantyne Farmer-Musselburgh; John Brown Teacher-Liberton.

Robert Forest Grocer-Midlothian; Wm Aitken Joiner-Walston: John Copeland Shoemaker-Lanarkshire.

In contrast to Haywood with its new way of life in mining, in the case of Auchengray it was a change of location not of occupation. All the tradespeople were those who served the farming community viz; farmers, joiners, shoemakers, blacksmiths and of course a grocer. Departing from this sequence was a tile maker.

Ages of those in employment varied' the youngest was James Brown age ten-cowhand. David Tweedie thirteen and a labourer on Ballantyne's farm. Wm.Tweedie, also thirteen, and a grandson of Wm Aitken, he too was an agricultural labourer.

At the other end one joiner Wm.Aitken was seventy three as was his wife.

There was no retirement age; of course they would work as long as they had the strength to carry on. There was no fixed school leaving age; school could be left behind at the desire of pupil or parent. There was a constant need for work hands by employers and the need to supplement the income coming into the home.

There was little change in the number of inhabitants by the 1891 census, neither had the occupation varied to any great extent. One noticeable feature was the absence of the same surnames in both years; in only one instance does the same name appear-Ballantyne father George in the first entry and his son John. This can be assumed by checking the son's age as one year old in 1851 and forty one in 1891.

An interesting case of 1891 is that of Wm Inglis - sixty three and wife Janet-sixty four. The son Wm and his wife Anne - thirty three and thirty four. The two families carried on the same trade as shoemakers. This Anne was my mother's aunt. She had the post office and provision, in the same building as the cobbler's shop and retained it till she died.

Regarding the format of the census itself there is little difference; one exception may have some significance-rank is included in the earlier heading. This has been deleted in the second.

Today the joiner's shop, post office and the grocer's shop have long since gone as has the blacksmiths.

Auchengray

While our story does not, to any great degree, find a place for the little place, it warrants a mention. Its importance lies in its contrast to the neighbours further north. It seems to be a natural link between the past and the future, and has a look of permanence and solidity that could not be claimed by the mining communities.

It has stayed the pace of change since the last century, with an unruffled calm. It is not disturbed by the 'progress' made by other communities. Like Tarbrax and Haywood, no pit reek or clanking machinery to interrupt its tranquillity.

But there are sounds and smells - all with a country accent. A farm is literally on its doorstep. The smell of leather from the shoemakers blend with the aroma of sweets, fighting with flour and groceries to subdue the stronger smell of paraffin; all under the same roof. The Inglis: Father and son had worked in this same house for around a century, at the same trade of shoemakers.

To my mind Uncle Willie was a gentleman with a beard. I claimed kinship with him, through his wife, who was an aunt of my mother's.

Stuart Provan (Lindsay) stayed all her life next door till she married. Her father was a nephew of the old man. She shares with me some respected memory of him. Her parents had the joiner's shop and house at the end of the little row, and was a favourite spot for a wee laddie from Haywood; to sit around and watch the brothers at work. The range of their products always amazed me. Timber buildings of all description; every kind of farm implement; they could even make a barrow for a boy of four.

Then there was the blacksmiths shop-the shoeing of large Clydesdales was an event not to be missed. The man, with his large leather apron round his waist and the foot of these monsters between his knees, nailing large special nails through the iron shoes, and well into the hoof of the horse. It took me some persuasion and time, to accept that it did not hurt the horse.

While there has been no development or industry, a few modern houses have been built, but the character of the village has not changed over many generations. There are exceptions; Who of a past generation would recognise the joiner's shop?

One thing that must have mitigated against it was the position of the village. Coal bearing strata lay to the north and east. Auchengray is situated on the high ground between Carnwath moss and Calder moor. So it has the advantage of looking down, and away to its more populous neighbours.

Like many other places; because of the fact it had been built before railways, it was strategically placed on the tracks and lanes of the old way of life. The brickwork was sited where there were conditions suitable for this purpose. The main railway for Edinburgh went through this point, as well as the branch line for Haywood and Wilsontown. So conditions were ripe for the development of the former two places, while it in itself, was too far away from this transport. The station was about one mile from the village.

One memory remains of the Inglis's shop; a Saturday visit every month. This entailed a long walk down the railway and up the cart track into the village. I can say there were few things about the visit that pleased me. To sit beside this gentle giant of a man who talked to you like an equal, instead of a stupid laddie. He seemed remarkably aware of what was going on in the area, and I was a ready listener.

Auntie Anne was the complete contrast. She was a birky and had a tongue that would clip cloots - my mother's expression. It had its drawbacks; there was nobody to play football with and very little reading material. A Moan and a girn was our summing up of the day. It would not have been so hard to bear if my father was there lending his support and company. He did not come often, and if he did it would be to escort us home via the railway from the junction; we very seldom took the train because it was a good way from the village and the fare was 1.½d. I never can remember it as being a real day out; you see, she very very seldom, gave any of the children a sweetie; this did not just apply to me and my sister. During a recent conversation with Mrs Provan (Stuart Lindsay) who lived next door in the joiner house and whose father was related to Uncle Willie Inglis.' Hand outs were rare and frugal'. I often wondered if she resented us not spending our penny pocket money in her shop. Nevertheless it would be unfair not to mention the teas supplied. They were special; mince pies heated in front of a clean coal fire that had been stirred up to give plenty of heat through the front bars where the pies were laid on a tray which hung over the bars. Weans got a half and adults a whole pie.

At school holidays my mother went over to give some help in cleaning the school. Jessie Lindsay did this. She had been married but her husband had been dead for some time. She was actually Mrs Kechans but I never heard her called anything but

Jessie. I liked these days; the run of the place with lots to do-sums on the blackboard and writing big words I had only recently learned, and plenty of books to read. It was a gold mine. I counted it a pleasure to run errands and carry the water for them. Jessie was kind to a wee laddie and my labour was always rewarded and she did not treat you as if you were a nuisance; you were somebody that counted with her.

Auchengray had its own windmill down in the field on the north east of the village. It took me a long time to believe that this was what pumped the water for the use of the residents. It could tell you how the wind was blowing and how strong it was. Alas like so many things, a feature and landmark, no longer dominates the field.

Travelling to Auchengray this gave the first sighting of an aeroplane. Hearing it for the first time, and when it passed over we raced to the highest point at which it disappeared in the distance. Conjecture was heated as to its starting point, and its final destination. Only two places rated a mention; Glasgow and Edinburgh. It was travelling from west to east. Our knowledge of local history was limited.

In a poem in my possession Willie Whitcomb is named as Wullie Wudlock. Even his proper name is spelled incorrectly; there is no 'e' at the end of his name. This piece gives some of Wullie's history and character relative to the Haywood, but I feel some of the information given might not be true e.g. George Paul says he was born in Addiewell near West Calder in 1864.

After some search at Register House in Oct.1995 along with an able assistance, I failed to discovery any evidence of his birth at Addiewell on the year stated. Indeed there is no record of his birth there in the five years previous nor in the five years after-wards. There is no evidence of his birth anywhere in Scotland.

174

His death certificate gives the following information he died on 12.3.38 at Omoa House Celland and was buried in common ground in Carnwath Cemetery on 15.3.38. His father's name is given as John Whitcomb as well as his occupation-police constable. His mother's name is given as Mary Stewart. With a name like Whitcomb, my assistant deduced he would be an Englishman, while his mother could readily be Scottish. If he was not born in Scotland it might also be true that he was born in England.

I followed this line of enquiry with an interview with Mrs. Maisie Baille now living at Calla Cottages opposite Calla Farm. She is the daughter of the late Mr and Mrs Peter Robertson, who farmed at Greenfield farm, between Auchengray and Tarbrax. This interview took place on Sat.21st 1995.

Willie did not stay every night at our farm. He covered a wide area in his travels, but he spent two or three nights with us. Forth, Wilsontown, Haywood, Auchengray, Tarbrax, Woolfords, and Cobbinshaw were local haunts but he went further afield West Calder and Addiewell in the east, and Lanark in the west.

I do not know if he ever slept at the Crooklands but he frequented Lindsay's joiner shop in Auchengray. The Lindsays were the kindest people you could meet and the Robertsons were the same.

My mother and father provided a bothy for him and he came and went as he pleased. My mother always had a fire lit for him every day and provided a bed. He would not sleep in the bed. He was always afraid he would fall out of it so my mother made one on the floor. He was never cold; plenty of blankets were provided. There was always bed and shelter for Wullie at Greenfield. He was not capable of much work about the farm. He was a simple soul; a man in whom there was no guile, and because of this he was the target of children's ridicule and fun.

My father arranged all his funeral affairs including the minister Rev. Mr Richmond Scott. After the funeral he said to my mother
"I should never have allowed Willie to be buried in Parish Ground. We should had a lair for him among oor ain folk."

He never ate his piece or meal without taking off his bunnet. (The writer can substantiate this. Never was he seen eating a piece at kindly folk's door, gala day, or Sunday school trips without uncovering his head.)

Do you remember his shirt stuffed with pieces. I don't know if he ever ate it all but his front was always bulging.

There was an Irishman stayed with us for a good long time as well. They shared the bothy; not very friendly. They just tholed each other. Charlie Collins did seasonal work at our farm as well as the surrounding ones. He outlived Wullie and died during the great snowstorm of 1947-48.

Wullie was very fussy about his boots and never went out without polishing them till they were shining. He gradually took over the boot cleaning for everyone here. He would never allow anyone to take over his job.

He was fond of bands and followed them whenever he could; at Gala Days and Carnwath Shows. I do not know when it all started but he liked to dress up in some old army tunic, or some cast off jacket of a bandsman. Another thing my mother always did for him; she had to sew tapes down the outside of his trousers to go with his jacket. He kept himself scrupulously clean. There was always an abundance of water on tap for him.

176

One of his regular features on a Monday morning was to bring his tin of coppers for my mother to count. If there was enough from his week's takings he would take the walk to Auchengray Station and then the train for Lanark market. Animals were his main interest on these occasions; there was no doubt that he would be looking to fill up his tinny. I do not think he would be refused at any doors.

I was not aware that he had stayed at Crooklands although I was aware that he did not come home to Greenfield some nights. I believe he was rejected by his parents owing to his simple nature. I have no knowledge of his parents living in Edinburgh; I certainly have no recollection of him visiting there all the years he stayed with us. I am not sure how long he stayed with us but he seemed to be there all my childhood.

We were not afraid of him; I think he was part of the place. He would eat mostly in the bothy but he liked a plate of soup. He never went hungry at our place. End of Maisie Roberton's version.

From an excerpt in the 'Reminiscences of Haywood' by George (Dod Donaldson) there that seems to suggest there is a flaw somewhere along the line of enquiry.

The late Mr. Ross the village constable found out where Willie had come from, to whom he belonged, so thinking to do him a good turn he took him to Edinburgh and delivered him to his home. Mr. Ross returned in the first available train and having to change at Auchengray the first person he met was Willie. He had returned on a goods train. From then on he was clothed and fed by the villages and farmers."

Come youths an bairnes one an' a'.

Frae Forth to Auchengray.
And spare a mindfu'thought or twa'
For Wullie that's away.
Nae Mairhe'll greet ye on the road
When gaun tae kirk or schule.
Nae mair he'll ask for pennies odd
His penny pock to fill.

Auld Wullie wi his ways sae droll
Attracted big and wee.
And Wullie filled a useful role
As well as you and me.

Wi' Wullie's wit, nane wid be fit
A ruler's post tae fill
Like Wullie we'd just dae oor bit
And dae mair guid than ill.

Auld Wullie he made freens wi'a
And enemies wi nane
And wis kent in every fearm and raw.
By mither, man, and wean.

At show and fair in colours rare
Just like a modern Jenny;
Auld Wullie will be missed I'm share
By them that gied a penny.

And wha sae base as would refuse
Tae help a brither chiel;
For Wullie didna weakness choose
And couldna help himself

When age and frailty in their turn
Kept Wullie off the road
The kindly folk at Greenfield Farm
Did much to ease his load.

To help the helpless on their way
Shows mankind at its best.
And Wullie would his tribute pay
For kindness like the rest.

Farewell then Wullie simple soul;
You're missed when you're awa'
But rest assured you filled your role
By gi'en us a ca'.

Another poem was printed many years ago;

When Willie first cam' tae oor glen
There's nane that kenned frae where he'd drappit.
A fresh complexioned callant then
Sae strong and sturdy. But ill happit -
His troosers tae the knees were slit;
His jaiket torn in mony places;
Au auld shae stuck on ilka fit
Wi' string as substitute for laces

He wasna wi'us many weeks
Till he began to look mair trigger;
A jaiket and pair o'breeks
Was gi'en him by Maister Biggar
Puir Wille dressed up in his braws
Wad ne'er ha'e ca'ed the king his kizzen;
To see him strutting roon the rows.
The weans, like bees, aroon him bizzin.

He never was a lazy loon
Although sae simple, saft, and silly;
There wisna mony in the toon
could shift a cairt o'coal wi Willie.
And whit for no-the meat he got
Was halesomer than maist folk wish it;
E'en suppin parritch oot the pot
Nor wad he let the guid wife dish it.

But oh the glee an happiness
When wi' the baun he was paradin
(The lover's ae' fond caress
Could hauf but cheer the heart o maiden).
His place was aye beside the drum
Wi' knots and ribbons roon his bonnet;
And Wae betide the venturesome
That daured tae lay a haun upon it.

But noo puir Willies failing fast;
He's no among us near sae aften.
Be kind to Willie till the last
Wha's simple weys your hert wid saften.
We ken that God will ne'er forget
A' them wha's road has been sae hilly
Should you a fit in heaven set
Amang the first ye'll meet is Willie.

Wullie Whitcomb
(Better known as Wullie Woodcock)

CHAPTER 15

EARLY DAYS IN DIRTY HIGHWOOD

As a family we had moved from Lesmahagow in the late winter of 1921, arriving after dark in the little village of Haywood – 'Highwood', in the Upperward of Lanarkshire.

The journey had been long and tedious, negotiating Kirkfield bank Brae, the main obstacle, after the tortuous road from the Nethan valley, over the hills to the Clyde valley. I was to hear of this many times from my sister who was six years old at the time. I was one. The sturggle with the loaded lorry up the brae, was for her the focal point of the expedition. It was to be recited so often during my infancy that I am sure I was word perfect; at least I remember it to this day.

My mother's account of these early times was somewhat different. She was to tell us of her dismay when arriving in the darkness, in a strange place of miner's rows huddled together or the face of the brae; no welcoming greeting that night but an injunction to my father. "You needna take the sticks off the lorry, ah'm no biding here." But of course they did come off, and they settled down for the night.

The morning was worse; daylight did not bring with it any illusions of grandeur. All it did was to illumine the dismal aspect of father's choice. Had he not been through to see the place, as well as securing a job in one of the local mines?

Surely he could not expect her to stay in this desolate place. Was not their house in their hometown on the banks of the Nethan beautiful? And more, it was near towns like Larkhall and Hamilton. They had a settled home in the Trows a part of Lesmahagow. It was to be a long time before she accepted this move as final. She quickly lined up the inhabitants of this dirty bleak, black place, with friends she had left in such lovely surroundings, much to the detriment of the former. Her verdict; "Full fou and fetch mair."

Later on I was to learn one of the reasons for staying; her simple philosophy was to say. "Never judge a circumstance or change by the initial experience, or a first attempt because of a failure. There was only one way out of this situation; take the branch line railway from Haywood to Auchengray, and so to home. It was the only means of escape to any life beyond", the only lifeline. She never took it.

Conjecture as to why they came is futile; sheer desperation at the creeping unemployment, may be been one. The pits were being worked out where they had lived. Word had come through on the grapevine of plenty of work in the Upperward of Lanarkshire, and Haywood was in the equation, so my father and his younger brother came here to find work, lodgings and look for a house. This they did, and soon they were on the move; the older moving first, the younger later with his larger family.

It is at this point that the story beings, and it is round the first family especially that the story revolves, as it reaches out and touches people, places and activities. It may have been that the decision was made easier by the fact that there was a Gospel hall in this new village. My family had been members of Hope Hall in Lesmahagow. They had many friends, and had settled down to take a part in that thriving community, and playing their part in the life of the town, my mother was loathe to leave. No wonder she told my father "Don't take the sticks off the lorry."

The house we came to was a two storied building housing three families, two facing west and the other looking towards the east. Our home had three apartments; two bedrooms upstairs and a kitchen with a scullery on the ground floor. (We did not talk about living rooms in these days, and of course scullery is long since been made obsolete.)

The kitchen had one set in bed with curtains that could be drawn if required, although these were mainly used for decorative purposes. A covering over the space beneath the bed was made usually of the same material. It was not considered fashionable if it did match the curtains. This space was quite commodious, the bed being about three feet from the floor. It was invariably used for storing things that were not in everyday use. Many and strange are the stories, true and ficti-tious about the contents of this secret hideaway. All miner's houses had this, so one would expect to see a wide range of articles in a place where outsiders were not allowed to look.

Seating in this room was quite basic; four wooden chairs were in our house. Apart from mother's rocking chair, a family heirloom it now has its home with my daughter in Maghera, N.I. the only chair made for comfort as well as usefulness was the big one. It was made of leather with arms and wings on it; these served a double purpose. It kept you free of the draughts from badly constructed doors and windows as well as providing a pillow for tired laddies who could curl up in it for a sleep, if father was not in at the time. The focal point in the room was the fire; it was very seldom allowed to got out. Backed up with a large piece of coal topped up with small coal called dross. This procedure was known as putting on the raker, raking up the fire for the night. But the real important bit of furniture for children

184

was the fender stool. This was a wooden seat that stretched the full length of the fireside and being only six inches in height was a favourite haven for resting. I can still savour the warmth and comfort of lying full length on this when I came home from school or play. You could sit on it as well, with your back against your father's knee as he sat in the big chair. It had a waxcloth covering as had the floor. (This was canvas finished off with wax. It was cold to bare feet, but this was offset somewhat by the rag rugs that were put at strategic areas. Our house always seemed to have plenty of these. The one at the fireside was larger than the rest, big enough to allow the bath (tub or bine) to be drawn up near the heat; you would step out on to the warm rug after your weekly bath, rather than on to the cold waxcloth.

These rugs were a blessing to bare feet, but there were drawbacks. They were hand made and home made.

Woollen material was used for these, and all kinds of clothing was plundered for this work. Worn out jerseys were favourites; but salmon pink drawers could be commandeered for this as well. Your skill as a housewife was gauged in some degree, by your efficiency in making a nice pattern. The permutations were endless, if bright coloured material was to hand, so it became a symbol as well as a sign of diligence and industry.

The long winter nights were spent on this task and all the family were caught up in this; rags had to be cut into strips as long as possible and a certain width. So a battle was on for rags, for there were not only other homes on the lookout for rags, but there was a delfman came round the doors at frequent intervals with his strident shouts. "Balloons for woollen rags; balloons for rags dishes for cooking and eating uses. Some of us acquired a complex about this, and felt very aggrieved at a heart as hard as mother's, but neither coaxing nor tantrums ever made any difference.

"T'is only rubbish he has; a wee balloon that will burst the first time you blow it up."

Going back to the fender; what a joy on a winter's night when my father would say "What about a story." He would then read another chapter of a book for children, one of my favourites "Joseph's little Coat' was the one I liked best. A tale of London, drink and poverty, and a boy that had never seen a green field, or heard a lark sing. Tears were frequent, but peculiarly these were the ones I enjoyed most. There may be others who frown on this exercise but I never felt anything else than a sympathetic affinity for him and an early realisation that `I was blessed with the home and parents I had.

Then there was 'Line upon Line' the story of Israel in children's form. How Abraham went out from Ur of the Chaldees, followed by Israel's history. The bondage in Egypt, the Passover, Red Sea and Jordan before they possessed the Land that God had promised them. Through it all a young mind came to the wonder that God did it all for them, although often they did bad things. So we proceeded to 'Treasure Island, Kidnapped' as school days arrived.

Our home was a Christian one. On the negative side there were things that were not done; drink was never in the house. Others might prove its mastery over them, but not here. Swearing was a bad word, and expletives were conspicuous by their absence in the vocabulary of our home. On the other hand, kindness and courtesy were installed in us by example, as well as word, but there was very little preaching done to exert an unhealthy effect on your impressionable minds.

But we were impressed. Most of my parents' friends in the village worshipped in the hall. In addition we soon learned that they had many friends outwith the little circle, and our home

186

was the haven for a broad range of men and women from much further afield; relatives and others they had known for years were regular visitors. It was thus early in life I came under the influence of itinerant preachers who stayed with us while taking a series of meetings. The speakers stayed in our home while visiting, for years.

This was not a home in the vice grip of dogmatism and legal binding to the law. Discipline there was, but it was balanced by kindness and love was the alchemy that touched and coloured our lives. It was a safe place might sum it up. It might be the target for cynical minds; looked upon as a place of restriction and prohibition, and of course there were occasions outside when, mixing with other children, and seeing their lifestyle so different from your own, that envy would rise, especially if the word 'Hallelujah' was hurled. I have fought the good fight with jacket off to dispel the idea that I was a soft touch.

These things were marginal and peripheral; deep down and perhaps well hidden, but none the less enjoyed, was the early developing sense that what you had was better than they had. Perhaps this led to a feeling of superiority, and probably governed your thinking. There were basics that were essential. Belief in God and his word were taken in as readily as daily food, and the facts of Jesus dying on the cross for sinners, and rising again and going back to heaven were of greater moment than the exploits of Wallace and Bruce and later events of our Scottish History; yes far more substantial.

While conditions in the home were basic, outside was far worse. Since running water was unknown there was no available water near except a barrel at the end of the house to catch the rainwater from the guttering round the eaves of the house. We called these rones. This water was not suitable for drinking so water had to be brought from another source. There were two; there was a pump down among the rows of houses, and a well down at Clarkswalls (The Den). This lay at the foot of a brae about half a mile away. It should be mentioned that there was a spring on the old railway just at the crusher bing on the path to Wilsontown, but this was small and you needed to lie down on your belly to get a drink. It was a spot you never passed without slaking your thirst. It rivalled the den for cold cleanness and a taste that belongs only to country springs. One wee boy summed it up recently. "We don't make water like that nowadays."

There was no drainage except open gutter (sheughs) Of course if there was no running water there was less need for drains except when heavy rains poured down for a full day. We were fortunate; living at the top of the village we did not need to contend with others dirty pollution. You could have races with pieces of twigs and any small objects that would float.

Because there was no water laid on. The question of toilets had to be solved. This was easy; there was a small lean to adjacent to the open midden to serve the three families. It was known as the dry closet. The adults in the houses took turns at emptying this in to the midden. This in turn was cleaned out at fairly regular intervals by a man from Forth with his horse and cart. When I was a boy I could not think of a worse job. Indeed the attraction of watching the operation, frowned upon by mother, soon lost its appeal, and we confined our activities to the glee of shouting names at the old man as he made his way down through the rows with his loaded cart. The word hygiene was not in our dictionary, relative to the disposal of waste. Nowadays we simply pump it into the sea along with the rest of our rubbish.

Eighteen people used this closet, but we considered ourselves lucky; over in the rows they had one for every row, probably thirty or more waiting their turn.

188

The Family

There were four children but the second oldest and the youngest died that year. They were buried, not here or Wilsontown among strangers but back home in Lesmahagow among their ain folk. One was two years old and the other a few months. This left my sister and me, it must have been a terrible time for our parents; it must have made them wonder if the move had been the correct one, but throughout all this struggle and heartbreak they kept with faith in their God. There is little doubt their spirit, indomitable and resilient, saw them through this trying experience, for they settled down quite quickly and soon made themselves part of the village life. They had found good neighbours. Indeed my mother too soon acquired the status of a competent midwife and was adopted on to the local service under nurse Cunningham and Dr. Reid. She used to tell us that the medical team left her to look after the patients. By this means doors were opened, quietly she won her way into the homes and hearts of the women folk.

Another thing that helped her to settle; she was soon co-opted on to the task of laying out the dead as well as the chesting (chistnin or kistin) putting them in the coffin assisting the undertaker.

She was a douce wee body, quiet and retiring in nature, and never argued on politics, local or national, but when anything affected her family she was not backward in fighting her corner.

What shall be said of my father? He was the dominant factor in the major moves they had ever made. When he made up his mind there was very little chance of anyone changing it. He was the oldest of a family of twelve; illegitimate, born to a young women in Rosewell, who worked as a brick moulder's assistant, while his father was a miner. He lived in

Auchendinny a few miles distance. They lived for years together before they married. There were twelve in the family. The last two were born in wedlock.

They seemed constantly on the move from this point onward; indeed twenty eight times was the flitting on the lorry. The whole range of the coalfield in the central belt was visited before my father married when he was twenty eight. No wonder the young wife was furious when confronting her husband about this move. She might have though that she was going to join the roundabouts without any hope of getting off. My grandfather did a lot of contracting, and these were the days when labour was cheap and expendable, while conditions and safety were minor considerations. It was a long standing joke in our family that the old man was running away from his past. What ever it was, was never discovered, and another point made that we were from the same line as the Buccleughs of Bowhill was always treated with a great deal of scorn and derision, although I did find out that my grandmother was born in Fushiebridge where her father was a land worker. He in turn along with his own parents had migrated from Hawick. Maybe there was a hint of mystery and romance about the story, sufficient to give some colour to drab hard lives and in young minds to plant dreams that have proved only that. A statement that was common in those days was as follows - "Born on the wrong side of the blanket"; with that we had to be content.

This constant moving as the family increased must have instilled in Matha a disinclination to spend time indoors, when he could be outside, and a desire for the open road and the fields beyond. He had been a miner since he left school, and all his working hours had been spent in the darkness and danger of pit and mine. Lights then were feeble affairs; an old oil wick lamp whose illumination rating must have been one candle power. This was stuck on a cloth cap. This was later to be

190

replaced by the famous carbide lamp, which really was a step into the twentieth century.

Is it wonder that the moors had a strong call and the sun, wind and rain had an ally in men like that. It was a love that he passed on to his family.

The pit was a necessity. No vocation this; the inevitable outcome of being born into a mining home, with no money, no prospects of any betterment and little chance of breaking the mould of family history.

CHAPTER 16

FIRST REMEMBERED CHRISTMAS

What would Santa give a four year old boy. He wanted a barrow; not any old thing knocked together from a few pieces of discarded boxes; a real barrow. A wood one with a steel rimmed wheel, painted inside and out. It would have his name on the outside in white letters to show up against the green while the inside would be red. My name would be in proper letters printed by a man who did that kind of work; not someone like my father who was just a miner. So it would be my very own and nobody would get a shot; well maybe not many but he would need to give Bert a chance. My mother would see to it that no big laddies would get their hands on it, for had she not said often during the autumn and winter when the event of Christmas was occupying young minds more and more and choices had to be made. "If Santa does bring you a barrow, Tom Dick and Harry have not to get it, because if big boys have it they will over load it, and soon it will be broken and fall apart.

My confidence in my mother's willingness to do what she could was absolute. Ah but there were other problems; she could not speak totally for Santa, and there were ifs and buts when approached about this, for surely Santa being a figure larger than life who lived at the North Pole had lots and lots of boys and girls to serve. "Maybe" was quite a favourite word with my mother, like wait and see, or "We'll see how bools now." I must have pestered her with my constant asking, and assuring her it need not be a big one; just a wee one for a laddie of four. Surely he could manage that.

Mind you there were other difficulties. How would he know? It was different from saying your prayers. God knew everything and could do anything so maybe he could fit in time to hear a prayer from a wee laddie about a barry among all the things you asked before you hastily jumped into bed as hurriedly as your prayer "This night when I lie down to sleep."

This would be four who would know how desperate I was for a barry; my father and mother, God and Santa. Even in the midst of doubt I could rely on my parents and maybe God. Santa was a different proposition, but as time went past the feeling of wonder and anticipation grew and optimism took over, but there was still that niggling doubt; how to get word to Santa Claus.

"Send a letter" said my father. "But I can't write yet. Where will we post it. At the post office" What is his address? Will it need a stamp" Again my father had the answer "I'll write it and you can copy it and a few days before Christmas Eve you can put it up the lum (chimney)." These were the days of coal fires and a special time had to be chosen when a new fire had been built and there was plenty of reek going up the lum. The secret was to throw it in among the reek and Santa was bound to get it. There was no need to worry. Mother may have said maybe; father never said that. It was either yea yea or nay nay. I always felt this was the difference between them. If father said we are going somewhere or doing something, as far as this lad was concerned it was already accomplished.

I did not want a big barry; I was just a wee laddie. Could Santa get it down the lum? Yes, there was room at the bottom but what about the cans at top? They did not look very big from

193

the ground: They were so far above you that you got a sore neck looking up at them.

Christmas Eve came. School was finished for big sister. She had not much time for a wee brother of four, worried about Santa; fact or fiction. Early to bed says mother. "He'll not come if you are not in your bed sleeping." Who could sleep at such a time? Was ever a night as this? Cuddled up in bed too excited to sleep and too scared to whisper unless under the blankets in case he heard and went by without leaving anything. Speak? You could hardly afford to breathe. Mind you we did not expect him to come upstairs. Had we not hung our stockings up by the fire where he would see them first when he came down the lum. So questions were asked. "Will he have come yet? Will we go down and see?" Big sister, with all the superiority of her extra five years, assured me that father had promised to wake them before he went to the pit (Miners did not have a holiday at this time and he always had time to engender the excitement and share the thrill of finding the presents).

"It must be rising time, we've been in bed for hours. Can we no go down and see?" "Ach allricht, but don't make a noise going down the stairs" Jean replied. So we slipped out of bed. The linoleum was cold to little feet. Down at the foot of the stairs you turned right and through a door into the kitchen. We did not have living rooms then. The scullery was straight on. With bated breath we stood and listened and then ever so gently big sister lifted the sneck and quietly pushed the door open to get a view of the room and the first thing we saw was father and mother sitting at the fireside; one reading and the other knitting and the stockings hung limp and empty. Before we got the door closed there was a voice from the fireside. "Who is at the door?" The spell was broken when mother called "Where are ye gaun at this time o'nicht. Get back to bed. It is only ten o'clock." We could not go back up the stairs without a heat at

194

the fire and a drink of milk before taking the long trek back to bed below the skylight window.

At last sleep came and we were roused by father standing at the foot of the bed saying "I thought you were not going to get up; do you want to see if Santa has been?" Magic moments to clear away cobwebs from eyes, and galvanise young limbs. So it was out of bed and a race for the kitchen. Mother was still in the set in bed. I don't think she was asleep; if she was, her peace was abruptly disturbed by the shouts "He has been here." And a rush to the foot of the stairs to meet father coming down. We greeted him with the same breathless news. It was only four o'clock.

You may ask why so early. Easy, father left the house every morning at half past four to walk to the pit some two and a half miles. He was a fireman and ran (inspected) the places for the colliers going down the pit just after six.

Yes he had been, you could see there was something in each stocking but a barry could not get in a stocking but it was there occupying the central place on the hearth rug along with Jean's present. You never saw a barry like this in your life. It was painted red on the inside, and green on the outside but best of all it had my name painted on one side. It was wonderfull; just what I had asked. How could he do it? Christmas must be special. It was perfect. My faith in Santa Claus, mother and father and God was completely restored. It was at this time I first began to see the difference between my parents. Mother's first words were cautionary. "Don't put anything heavy in it or you'll break it" These came hard on father's exclamation. "You'll can hurl lots o'stuff in that barry."

No question as to how it got down the lum. Santa could do anything so it was no problem to get a wee barry down. It was the best one ever made. Mind you my knowledge at that time

195

was limited. There was a barry at Barrie's farm and one at the station. They were far bigger but did not match this new model. The one at the station was all chipped and scuffed and looked as if it had never been painted while the one at the Crukens was what you would expect of a dung barry, dirty and smelly. Mine would never get like that. I would wash it and polish it every day and indeed I was told that I kept my promise for a full week. This barry finds a place further on in the story. The contents of the stocking were then pulled out. There was not a great deal more, an apple and orange with a chocolate and a new hanky. If all things are relative; at that age you could not be happier. Could kings and queens be as we were on that wonderful morning?

Perhaps the person that got most pleasure from this great event was my father, and this set the tone for all events and relationships with him. He made every event special with his own brand of enthusiasm and enjoyment, and in the future, was to prove this over and over again, as he entered into all the games in or out of doors.

He was the one who kept the football blown up and patched if necessary. He was chief dragon(kite) maker, plan and organise a Halloween Party; trail the fields with you looking for bird's nests. What of the Glasgow Fair Saturdays and Mondays when he saw to it that these two days of idle time were put to good use for his family; yes and one or two others- Edinburgh on Saturday and Glasgow on the Monday. New Year for me was quite special. Form earliest days I would go with him to Motherwell conference to hear great speakers on the first of January and on the second it would be the City Halls Candleriggs Glasgow for a repeat. One might question the wisdom of this. As a boy I never did. It was a privilege to go; maybe it was the tea at half time that counted more than the preachers. I made the choice. Nevertheless there were spin-offs

196

from this; I was learning discipline as well as unconsciously imbibing some of the preaching of the Bible.

We had always enjoyed family life and Christmas was only one of many occasions throughout the year that was special. I might bicker if I had to take my wee brother on walks and ploys, and girn if big sister made it quite clear that absence was preferable to your company, but home and family gave young lives stability and security.

It may sound boring and trivial at this time, but to us it was never anything else but safe, when night came and the door was shut. Add that to the glow of the oil lamp sitting on the table and everyone doing something within the range of this limited light. The table was always drawn up near the fire but invariably, the fender was the place to be. Hot on one side. It was not so draughty as sitting at the table, although most of the activities were centred on it.

It was a plain wood table scrubbed white with years of service. Most never had a cover, but ours did for meals have an oil cloth cover. There were things that were accepted without questions. The big chair was father's if he was at home. If you were sitting in it when he came in you never needed to be asked to rise. I have always had reservations about this but the pecking order never changed. Another thing that emphasised his position was in the serving of meals. His plate was filled first, then the children were served, with mother taking up the last and mostly the smallest portion.

Looking back it does not seem right but it was the recognised order. The reason given was that the man in the house was responsible for the upkeep of the house and family and as such had to be first and well fed for work in the pit; the children were growing weans and needed plenty of good nourishing food. I still cannot understand why mother came last in the food chain, yes and in many other ways as well, when her task was the hardest of all. She did the housework and cared in every way for the brood in her nest. There were no latch key children in these days; neither were there hoovers or washing machines for dirty clothes or dishes. The amount of work done had to be viewed in the light of the size of the families. Where ten or more were in the home; of this number two could be under five. Five could be still at school while there might be three colliers joining their father at the pit.

Pit clothes had to be brushed and dauded against the outside wall if they were dry; if wet they had to be dried before the fire. Pit boots were always polished by the housewife for the sake of her standing in the village. It has been known for a woman to have six or more pairs of boots polished and laid out in the evening sunshine at the door. You see it preserved the leather. The advent of the pit baths changed all that. Men who would not be seen going to work without a shine on their boots before, soon learned to keep them in the lockers at the pit and they never were taken home.

Mother had also the task of laying the clothes out for the morning. This was always a bone of contention. Quite often the first to get up claimed the best and the devil took the hindmost. Tempers were not at their sweetest at that time in the morning when faced with another hard shift following a late night. We are thinking of five in the morning. Wives were in the main responsible for the pieces, normally four slices in a tin box made to take plain bread although many took six or eight. The biggest I have ever seen was Duncan's; he carried twelve slices.

The greediest I have ever known involved a father and a son working on the same shift in the same section. The father was always in first to this work and after hanging his bag up in the

198

main road went up the faceline, without taking a bite (it was customary to take a bite and a drink out of your tin flask before starting, although this was discouraged by he management.) The son came in among the last, ate his father's piece and drank his tea. He always made sure he was out for his piece before the old man and scoffed his own and back into his work before his father came down the face. This continued for a few days till some of the men noticed this and told the deputy. He in turn informed the man. So the free pieces stopped for the glutton, although the father continued to keep a couple of slices for his laddie.

Getting washed before you ate was not always the norm. This is where the fender played its part. You sat down at the table for your dinner then you stretched out on the fender and so sleep for a few hours, before rising, washing and getting ready for bed. This was never practised in our home since my father was the only person working in the pit in those early days. In an age when things were not so open as they are now, how did they manage to preserve their privacy, when sex was a word you learned outside the home from class mates and big brothers.

There might be some girls; their task was to serve father and big brothers. In a word to follow in mother's footsteps, assume many of her tasks, until they too became mere chattels to father and brothers. The only hope of escape was to leave home and go to domestic service, but most came back to marry local pit lads, and keep the cycle going for another generation. A few were strong enough to make a clean break and only come back for holidays; these fortunate ones gradually drifted away from the village and made a life for themselves outside the confines and culture of "pit claes and parrich." (A term often used to describe the first shift after a holiday or idle time.)

CHAPTER 17

SCHOOL

It was raining cats and dogs the day I went to school for the first time. My big sister Jean took me, calling in for her friend Maisie Graham whose young brother was also starting out on this great adventure. Robert was to go through school years in the same class, and was to prove in years to come that he had a natural talent for all kinds of ball games.

I had a new pair of wellington boots, a revelation to me and a source of boasting. I could go anywhere, and not get my feet wet; not only through puddles but in the station burn. In days to come this same stream was to test them, and on occasions of heavy rain, water could lap over the top, bringing retribution at home with accompanying threat that they would be put away and tackety buits ordered a threat that always materialised unless you stuck to the rules.

A strange place a school; all sitting quietly two at a desk boys and girls separated. The final indignity was to be made to sit beside a lassie. This punishment was usually meted out for some serious misconduct or some schoolboy howler. What shame and ignominy from which you suffered for days from classmates.

The early days passed slowly but 'The cat sat on the mat' gave way to real books without pictures. Add to this there was learning by not racing through the two, five and ten times tables, and stuttering at the more difficult, like the seven and nine. This type of teaching is frowned upon today, but it was very effective and was a basis for arithmetic during primary school.

The head teacher, Miss Lambie and her assistant and junior Miss Goddard made up the staff of the school. The last headmaster had left before the summer holidays. Before the building of the school, children had been taught by two teachers; Mr Brown and Mr Kerr. This was done in a house that was later occupied by Dr Thomson in the School Row next to the place where the new school was built. There were to be three more headmasters before I went to school viz. Mr.Biggar, Mr McIntosh and Mr Yuille.

I did enjoy school and reading did not present any great difficulty for had I not sat on my father's knee or on the fender while books were read to me. So there was the joy of learning to read properly and the triumph of reading round the class; better still if teacher asked me to read a part with big words.

Pupils never got very near to the teacher. You could not risk being called a 'sook' by the rest of the class. It always seemed to be a case of them and us; a continuation of our pre-school training that you did what you were told and in some ways made to appreciate that it was wrong to step out of line.

Nevertheless you listened and you learned, and in all my schooldays I only ever found one was a sadist; that was at the secondary school at Forth. He flourished the belt indiscriminately and with real venom. A pupil was to be the recipient of some startling news, when travelling by bus, the master should sit down beside him and regale the ex-pupil with the information that there were times when he could not get out of his mind, what he had done over the years. He suggested he was lucky in the age when he taught, that he had not been up for cruelty.

Apart from that time I always felt school was an extension of home discipline, which I never felt was coarse or brutal. This did not prevent us shouting as a group of us made our way home, but well away from the sharp ears of the teacher, our favourite chant about the school.

"Highwid is a bonnie place
It stands upon a hill;
The only thing that's wrang wi' it
Is auld Jean Lamie's skule.'

While school hours were not usually a bore, my mind was out in the playground, or on to the further fields that stretched from our front door to secret haunts. Clear to my mind is the playground; boys and girls separated by a brick wall with a gate from each on the road. The main part was square and sloped down from the gate to a long level patch at the bottom; no tarma-cadam just plain earth hardened by tramping tackety boots.

While the top half was unsuitable for football, the presence of beech trees was perfect for hide and seek, cowboys and indians, and marbles.

There were games that had their seasons, but football was the perennial favourite. Sides were picked every Monday morning, the sides chosen lasted the full week. The older ones always seemed to be on the same side. This meant that the younger and smaller were relegated to the opposition. This was easily seen by observant young minds to be a blatant attempt by the older to subject the wee laddies to a humiliating defeat by the end of the week. Play went on every break time, and scores accumulated till Friday. It was a formidable score line. But this was soon to be changed. There was a new crop of youngsters coming through when I went to school. My cousins next door were all players with natural talent.

202

The older ones in the family recognised this and there was soon an established order that overthrew the past regime. With Robert Graham added to the team we made a good squad. Football to us all was the main reason for living. Being educated was just one of life's disciplines, and if you happened to like it, so much the better, but prowess in the class was nothing compared with the success on the field of play. Who amongst the boys did not thrill to the sound of the bell of release to the freedom of the outside, and cry "Whaes goat the ba?" It would then be produced from someones pocket; he was the one who had the ball at his feet when the bell rang to call us to our labours. No it was not a team ball, but an unburstable one-a penny or two pence at the most. By this time I got a football every Christmas; not allowed to take it to school. Mother's injunction was always the same "You are no takin your fiba tae school; it widnae last a week." Balls had to be made of unburstable material owing to the containing walls. It was only a fairly narrow strip bounded on three sides a five foot wall and at the other, by the end of the classroom with windows. This made for one touch play; as well as educating us in the principle of keeping the ball low. I never remember the ball hitting the windows, although one summer day it was kicked through the open window when the two teachers were standing watching our exhibition of skill, or more probably ensuring us that we were aware of their presence, even during our period outside. Maybe I misjudge them. They were both excellent teachers throughout my primary days.

There were two reasons for keeping the ball low. If you did kick it over the wall even if it was inside the goals it was not allowed as one; too high; in addition you had to run up through the gate and round into the farmers field to retrieve it from the long grass; all this time the waiting boys kept up a catcall of advice and doom laden threats, as to what would happen if you did not find it. "You'll no be playin the morn, or if you are, you'll be goalie."

Worse still if you kicked it over the wall into the girl's playground. There would a great squealing and a refusal to hand it back. It could be handed in to the teacher at the end of playtime. It was an early instruction into the wiles of girls and women, for boys were not allowed into the girls playground.

The second lesson you learned, was to use the walls to your own advantage by dribbling along the side of the brick wall and as you were tackled you had two options; either pass him on his left side or hit the ball against the wall and retrieve it as you flashed beyond his tackle.

Perhaps today's players should be taught more of these skills with a wee ball. These were the days of Allan Morton-the wee blue devil-considered by many of us as the best in the world. No Sunday papers in our house, but there was always a quick dash round by No.8 now for the Daily Record on Monday to see how Rangers got on, Saturday. Especial jubilation if the opponents were Celtic. How this bias come about is difficult to explain, for while there was evangelical preaching every Sunday in the hall, and home was a continuation of this exercise, I never heard any allusion to the differences between people in our home. In a predominantly Protestant environment it was easy to take sides with the majority, and so close out others who were different. For me it did not extend to school either. Play was a matter of fun without bigotry.

One of the things I did resent was the Bible lesson and the Catholic children were allowed out. They as much as the rest were just as upset because it heightened the awareness of this gulf. Envy on our part would be the predominant feature. It was not so much anti-Bible feeling but a grouse that some were getting away half an hour earlier. Eager for the bell to ring the end of another day, the last thirty minutes stretched away into infinity, but at last; out and away to the freedom of the open road home and the fields beyond where you could shout your loudest, without a whispered command to be quiet. You were free to use your own language which was not allowed in school and play your own games.

Home; to throw off the bag and slip out to play without mother noticing. Some hope mothers do have eyes in the back of their head, for this ploy never worked. There would be the inevitable cry. "Robert get into the hoose and get your auld claes on." Well it was worth a try. This meant taking off your jersey and trousers with the added burden of pulling on old patched garments that were deemed too old for school. There was always her stock reply about any complaints. "These is nae shame in a patch but there is in a hole."

We did not get into a great deal of serious trouble, but mischief has always been second nature to boys and girls. There was no mugging-common today - G.B.H. was not a common term then. There could be fights if a man got drunk and wives and weans would suffer, but to my knowledge these were of an infrequent occurrence.

Discipline was instilled down through a hierarchy that started with a healthy respect; indeed a fear of the police if you did not behave. One especially stands out. With his big Alsatian dog and his sterness made you think it would not be a good thing if he caught you doing damage in any shape or form.

Teachers carried far more authority than they do today, but it should be understood that the belt in most cases was not flourished indiscriminately, and there was no use going home with a sob story about unfair teachers. Mothers, replies were always the same. "You must have been needing it, or you would not have got the belt". No, teachers did not suffer from stress and did not need counselling or early retirement. The stress was weighted against the pupil, and at the country school I never remember an irate mother at the gates determined to take a strip off a teacher.

The home might be the last in the chain of command but in reality it was at the forefront of the struggle to equip you for the big world outside, and one thing you learned was the truth that discipline was all part of caring, loving parents, who made you aware of standards. These had to be set there if a decent life was to be had by all.

Teachers could not be replaced or sacked if they slapped a pupil on the back of his head. One girl was asked if she would like to be a teacher when her university career was finished "A teacher; you would need a policeman on one side and a soldier on the other."

CHAPTER 18

OTHER GAMES

Each season brought its own crop of games which could be played by boys and girls but football was the perennial favourite and was essentially male orientated. Although when speaking to Mrs. Mary Watson (Maimie Brown) recently I learned of her objection to playing in goal; this part kept her out of the real thrill of the game and she had resented this very much. Glad to know you did not bear grudges; it was a lovely tea you provided the day I called. Hide and seek, kick the can, run sheep run, were communal games, where girls could give as good an account of themselves as the boys.

On thing I hated as a wee laddie was when you were picked to be the the one who chases in children's games. This was a great game if you were big and fleet of foot, but if you were young and wee as well you could be het all night as the bigger boys and girls kept kicking the can away when you had left the den looking for hidden culprits. By the time you had recovered the can everybody was well hidden and so you went through the same again. It was a refined form of torture in the name of a game. Tears of frustration and anger would flow and they were never dried, by threats of banishment from other games if you decided you had had enough and ran home to mother with your tale of woe. A special cuddle and an assurance that she would speak to your big sister. But nobody was to know of the comfort of a mother's hug and the promise that nobody would see the tears or your complaint of such ill treatment. Big boys don't cry was the final answer as she wiped your eyes on the corner of her apron.

Handball was also popular with the boys. The gable end of my Aunty Kate's house was ideal for this. There was a stretch of bare ground right along the wall. The game was played after this fashion; a chalk line some four feet high was marked along the wall and the area of play was marked as well by scoring your foot along the ground. An old tennis ball or an unburstable one like that used at the school was ideal. It was played by two people much in the way tennis is played. Some of the lassies became very good and could hold their own with the laddies. It was a summer game and was mostly played in dry weather.

Cricket never caught on. The football pitch was too lumpy and too many threshes made the game impossible. As a boy into reading all the books I could lay my hands on I always dreamed of going to a public school and being Captain of the first XI. I would score a century against a toff school who thought we were only there to make up the numbers. There was always a snag; all these schools played rugger. No good, it had to be one, where real football was played with a real team ball. Then there were marbles or bools, another fair weather sport which needed special skills. The two kinds, glesses and bools; the former were used for hitting and the other were for putting in the line, or in the moshie holes three in number in a straight line. Our favourite was the bools on the line. In this each player had to put a bool on the line. There was a certain distance picked and turns were taken to throw a marble up. The glesses nearest a bool got first plunk (to do this you caught your marble between the point of your index finger and the knuckle of your thumb). By this means you could propel it at a fair speed. If you did it with the marble between the nail and the inside of your finger it was not nearly so effective; this was known as

208

using poussie knuckle. No only did you get a bool if you hit a bool on the line but if your turn came and there was an opponent's marble within striking distance you could hit it, so sending it further down the line and also he had to pay you a bool out of his pooch (pocket). This was for me the least popular game for it could be quite expensive if you were not particularly good at it. These implements had to be purchased out or your Friday penny. Need I say more.

CHAPTER 19

HIGHLIGHTS.

Special events and dates were severely rationed, but because of this they assumed for us an importance that set them apart from ordinary days. These occasions were the jewels in the necklace of everyday affairs and commonplace happenings. Who can tell the agony of long intervals of waiting when days crawled by on leaden feet, and the mounting excitement as the time drew near and the thrill of being wakened on the morning of the event. Christmas has already had an airing but what about New Year? No work for father for he had the first and second of January off-not a holiday, although it was posted as such at the pit. Men were free although the holiday was not. It simply meant two idle days. Oh yes the owners were magnanimous; they gave you four days off work; two at the Glasgow Fair and two at this time. You had to either save up for this or simply tighten your belt. In our case the former was always true and followed the same patterns. This for me was a time of real enjoyment; the first day spent at Motherwell conference in the Town Hall with four speakers with an hours interval for tea. When you were young you did not appreciate the preaching. It was not up to much but the tea; great stuff especially if you sat next an old lady who did not care very much for pies, but liked the spiritual food. So both of us were satisfied when she whispered "Wid ye like my pie" and sometimes it stretched to a fern cake or an eiffel tower as well. The loaves and the fishes had nothing on this.

Nevertheless it was not all pies and pastry; there was the acquired knack of learning to sit quietly and gradually you absorbed knowledge unconsciously and it became part of the great process of growing up. A simple foundation was laid in those early years and the true statement had much merit.'Train up a child in the way it should go and when he is old he will not depart from it.' Environment and early training do make a difference in most cases, and are real forces to be recognised. Speakers like Harold St John W.E. Vine, E.W. Rodgers and W. W. Feriday and other stalwarts whose name have been remembered by countless numbers; not forgetting our own wee Scots undermanager Robert Prentice who ranked with the best. These were rich pastures for young minds which stretched as you listened, till you were able to understand for yourself the unfolding of the great truths of the Bible, until it became for you the final authority and the great arbitrator. These days were times of discipline as well as enrichment.

I firmly believe that those attending these kind of meeting were the best taught; not thrilled to one man's ministry, but enriched by teaching from men whose whole life was spent in the study of this book. Thus there was a broader base and a wider range acquired by the audiences and this lead to a deepening of the spiritual content of your life.

There was always the danger of egotism creeping in, both in speakers and learners and a self righteousness that was both spurious and false; a kind of humility of which you would be proud

One thing I can remember; the visit at the New year quite often meant an overnight stay at an aunts in Holytown so I was privileged to go to a hogmanay social with singers as well as preachers. There was no price for tickets but a collection by passing a bag round - not a plate - the right hand had not to know what the left hand did. One night at the end of the service a man and wife with four children in tow stopped to speak to my father and observed. "A grand night Matha and it only cost a tanner (sixpence)." The reply was terse and to the point. "Aye and somebody had to pay the rest." Adults are dim and wee ears are sharp.

Then there was possibly the zenith of my experience; Glasgow Fair Saturday and Monday. The first day we were off to Edinburgh with the eight o'clock train changing at Auchengray on to Princes Street; having a close look at Cobbinshaw Loch in the passing. We had only seen this from a vantage point up near Mountain Blow Farm and after two or three trips we knew that we were near our destination when we saw Murrayfield and Jenner's depository.

Oh! The crowds, jostling and pushing. It was worse than seeing who would be first into the field at the Sunday School trip. Then there was the tram; it had to be open topped - first on and up the stairs and right to the front feeling cheated if someone was already there. We did not really need seats. They were superfluous for you stood up all the way. There was no thought of others; you were going to enjoy this day suppose it was the last thing you did. Where was the tram going; no need to ask for it never varied from year to year. The Zoo was the terminus for us.

This was a different one from our limited view of three things, fields and animals, ponds and burns with frogs (puddocks) and Minnows (Mennens) wide skies and birds. We certainly had gates and fences to keep farm animals from straying. Here there were high fences and stone walls which meant restriction and confinement. Animals larger than we were used to seeing running around the doors at home.

212

Then there was the picnic; sitting on the grass with sandwiches and milk from home. We did not pay for this or any other entertainment. Father had made provision for all eventualities, but sweeties and ice cream had to be paid for out of your savings of a penny every Friday. This bank had been accumulated painstakingly and self sacrificially over the weeks prior to the 'jant'. Therefore it could not be squandered prodigally in the first shop but was doled out in halfpennies. It had to last all day.

Father had a great sense of enjoying the outing even more than the children and as we finished our pieces he would say. "Where will we go now." He as well as the children knew the answer. "Portabello for a dook in the sea" was the united response and another scramble up the stairs to the front seats. It was a journey and a half past the Caley station again on Princes Street. The castle, not to be visited this time. What was an old castle stuck up on a rock compared to the sun sea and sand of the magic of Portobello beach. The crowds here were worse than at the station or the Zoo. Did you ever see the like. What if you got lost? Would you ever be found? The sharp fear of it led to the deeper enjoyment of the adventure but you kept a tight grip of his hand nevertheless. You looked for a bare bit but these were at a premium. So you added to the crush by squeezing in with the rest. Immediately it was off with the clothes and into a homemade pair of pants. In seconds you were in over the head and shouting to the laggards in the party. "It is great come away in, coordie" You shouted this even though your teeth were chattering and you were shivering. Was it ever warm in the sea at Good old Porto? Another thing that weighed with you; you would never live it down if you went home and admitted you had never been in for a dook (swim).

Perhaps our enjoyment or endurance was made all the better by the fact that dooking holes were scarce in Haywood and needed a lot of rain to fill the dams that were laboriously built. The burns here were near their source.

One memorable visit we went to the baths. I was just school age and I was overawed by the splendour and size. I will never forget it. I had not learned to swim and was playing in the shallow end, while father was ploughing up and down with his favourite breast stroke. He encouraged me to come into the deeper water. After a few minutes he suggested I got on to his back and he would swim round the pool keeping near the side if I was afraid. Afraid; I was terrified. I could not swim and the water was six feet deep. Over against that, was the fact that I had watched with envy his swimming, and my constant faith in this man who was my father, overcame my fear, so I got on to his back and he swam round keeping near to the side as he had promised. After a time I was brave enough to say "Go doon the middle faither" which he did.

Going back to this story; the day was not finished. Back on to the tram and off to the gardens to hear the band. There was not much music in our family. The old Sankey hymn book or the Redemption songs was the context and boundary of our musical aspirations, so it was the colours and the crowds that made this music worthwhile

Then it was a bee line for the station. By this time there was a niggling doubt about the train. "Are you sure that is the time of the train and are you certain it stops at Auchengray?" It had been a great day but if the last train went away without us what would we do? It never did; we always made it with plenty of time to spare. Being early had its advantages; a corner seat facing the engine. It was twilight now and had deepened to darkness when we heard the shout of a porter. "Auchengray change for Haywood and Wilsontown. It was a Saturday and there was no early rising for the school.

The pleasure was enhanced by the presence of sister and her two cousins while Bert their young brother and my best pal

214

made up the party. It was a case of: *'Serve sma'. Serve all.'* We all find in life that a pleasure shared is a pleasure doubled.

At home for the Sunday. Even it was different. No Sunday School - one day off in the year-but all this was irrelevant. Tomorrow was the sole concern; get through Sunday and let Monday come as quickly as possible. Yesterday's experience was already receding in the light of a new adventure.

The seven train in the morning, an hour earlier than Saturday. We changed at Auchengray with a quick rush over the bridge for the train for Carstairs. Yes but that was but another change for the Glasgow one. This was better; Oh the thrill of waiting on the platform for the arrival of the London express and then the wonder of seeing this monster for the first time, with its power and steam. No two carriages and no old 17323 with a high lum, it had come all the way from London stopping only at Crewe, Carlisle and Lockerbie. It was a dilemma; count the carriages twelve in number, time to see the driver at Glasgow Central. What a job controlling this huge engine. "I'll be a driver when I grow up; never a fireman straight to the driver's job. Look at him, shining cap as he looks down on the passengers."

What a journey this was going to be, but you were caught up in the anxiety of getting a good seat and counting the number of carriages. This was adventure indeed. At last I got on, holding tight to my father's hand and a long the corridor. This train had flush lavatories; we did not even have them at home. I had other things new to me. It had first class on some of the doors. I knew enough not to try and get into one of these; they were reserved for the big bugs, but mind you it would be marvellous if you could get the chance. They even had white things up behind their heads.

The whistle from the guard and the notice of this great train moved slowly out of the station. Only one stop: no wonder it was called an express. Motherwell was reached before I had got over the joy of this new way of transport and soon we were drawing into Central. In Glesga where the Rangers played and of course this was the home of Alan Morton. I'd never seen him, but I had read about his feats from the Daily Record every Monday morning.

We were off the train and down to the Broomielaw for the boat. This was another wonder; then it was off 'Doon the waatter to Dunoon.' The journey down this great river was something apart. To see huge ships in the making and recall what I had learned about the making of the great Empire, and this added to my scanty knowledge of Glasgow's engines that also went all over the world especially to the parts that were coloured red in the atlas at home.

Then it was down to see the engines; the great big steel shafts racing backwards and forwards. This was to give way to the green shoreline and the hills beyond. Maybe I got my first thirst for these hills towering to the sky which was later whetted on countless visits up till the present time; or was it an extension of the fields at home with their view of the distant Pentlands.

I thought the crowds at Edinburgh were large; nothing like this. The whole of Glasgow was on this boat; there was hardly room to move, and I was not too sure that it was safe but I soon settled down when NOBODY ELSE SEEMED CONCERNED. There was a band playing going down and back. Dunoon did not rate a mention in comparison with Edinburgh but it was a greater joy getting there. Tired but happy when the train was on its way but a bit worried if it would stop at Carstairs. No hitches, but I had no learned then to let the train take the strain. Would it not have been terrible if it had no stopped. It was an express bound for London; the next stop Lockerbie.

I would need to find out how far it was to that distant place. What a joy to stop and hear the same porter as the one on Saturday shouting the same warning. Yes he did not need to call out twice; we were out, and into the waiting train before father got his second wind. Darkness and time were important. This was impressive; A train in the darkness with sparks flying high into the night sky, and up later than you ever were at other times. This ended the day to beat all. "I'll tell you all about it tomorrow, mother;" too sleepy to loiter, but up the stairs to the wee room under the skylight. No light was needed Jean and I knew where the bed was.

The next day was a repetition. I do not think I ever stopped to think of the rest of my pals as I trotted out the happenings of the day. It was a very limited number of children who ever got a day like this. As children as with adults we ride on the crest of our own little sea of our experiences, failing to realise what you would be like if the roles were reversed.

The other main highlights of our year were the Sunday School trip and the Soiree. The former held in one of the local farmer's field. The farmer, his wife and family, along with the servants put themselves about to make the day special. Swings had been put up in the haysheds; there were crossbars for pillow fights and plenty of sacks for the races with a good supply of strong ropes for tug of war. It was a full day event with two meals provided. Milk was supplied for this in sufficient quantities to give a tinnyfull to children who preferred it to tea.

One of life's lasting memories was the tinny on a piece of tape around your neck and as the name suggests it was made of tin and hot tea made it impossible to hold, far less drink out of it. I can never remember anyone ever being scalded. It was a miracle. Sitting down in rows was mandatory. No order, no tea, so after a few choruses the grace was said by the superintendent. Some of these chorus's have never been forgotten. "The birds upon the tree tops sing their song. Give me oil in my lamp keep it burning." Then came the treat of the trip. Tea and buns were served but again rules had to be observed. Rigid discipline was accepted. You sat where you were placed in your row and were supplied in your turn. This prevented accidents. There always seemed to be enough for all. Nothing to pay; of course you had to attend Sunday school or there was no ticket for the trip. Some of the children tried to circumvent this by coming along for one day before the outing but this was soon rectified. I do not know if it was a recognising by the teachers of the unfairness of this, or the regular pupils complaints. To us it was a devious thing that should not be allowed. I think you had to attend for ten Sundays before you qualified.

It was all geared to get the boys and girls out-a form of bribery; a reward might be deemed a better term, but in the main it worked because it was made easier by the attitude of the parents. They would be pleased to get the weans out from among their feet to give them a hour's peace in a home where there was a proliferation of children. The same rules applied to the Soiree.

Prizes as well as tea could be had if you were a good attender. These prizes were not handed out indiscriminately. Three types were used-first second or third costing 2/6; 2/-; 1/6- perfect attendance; one Sunday off and two Sundays off. Now there was the subject of the where withall to finance these outings. It must be realised that there could be eighty pupils. This added up to a fair sum.

Wages were not big and most members were miners with fairly large families of the congregation, so with very few if any wives working things were tight all the time. Perhaps it would be right to say that in these early days in Haywood and Wilsontown, the members would number in their twenties. This would give some indication of the generous nature of this little band and their concern for the welfare of the children of the village. Some may question all this but until I find a better substitute for the Sunday School I will retain my position. Of course none of the men folk would drink and very few smoked so this must have helped the exchequer.

The Soiree was always held in December. As with the summer outing mothers and fathers were allowed to attend; indeed were encouraged by the fixing of the price of a ticket at rock bottom prices. This was the night when their offsprings would be doing their parts-recitations, singing. This in itself was a magnet for big folks. Was there ever a parent who did not see in their own prodigy a budding genius? All the saying and singing had a spiritual slant although some carried a bit of humour. Title like the Sunday Skill Soiree, some of the lines are with me yet "trying to serve them aa at yince."

At the 'Sunday School Soiree.' Some were more serious and one in particular entitled 'Wee Jimmy Douglas" the covenanting boy taking food to an old man holed out in a cave in a glen. He was apprehended by the "Bluidy Claverhoose." This was frightening indeed. Lines like "I'll throw you down where carrion crow will battle for your bones." And Jimmie's fearless reply "Cast me doon there if ye will. It's no sae deep as hell." Strong stuff even for us who had a real affinity for Jimmy.

Tea was always served first so back to the tinny and the poke of buns. The same strict discipline was observed and no remembrance of any accidents. Things were looser during this period and after the tea and cookies were finished there was a competition who could blow up the bag and burst it with the loudest bang. After tea and the pupils dramas, there came the high point for some; those who would get a prize. The thrill of hearing your name called out First prize to.......for a perfect attendance completed a great night or nearly so; there was still something to come as you left the hall. A box of Macintosh apples and a box of oranges on either side of the door with teachers in attendance and you were given a choice; an apple or an orange. What a night.

Maybe it is from scenes like these too, Auld Scotia's grandeur rise.

We belonged to the British Empire and this owned most of the world. I knew by the amount of red in the atlas at home. Not only so you had been taught all about Lucknow-its relief. Khartoum and all about General Gordon with the Boer War thrown in for good measure. Nothing was taught of the 1914-1918 War to end all wars. It was too recent an event.

More was made of Wallace and Stirling Bridge; Bannockburn and Robert the Bruce and of course Flodden had a mention.

Nothing was made of our heritage as a mining community or rural living. We were never told of the loss of lives in the pits and the crippled and maimed from wars and pits. At school we learned history and geography written by the victors not the victims. In our house we learned that Calvary was the only Battle where the apparent victim wrote the history of the conflict; not with paper and pen, but in the hearts of men, women and children.

Of course this is old stuff and we no longer subscribe to it. If this be so; are we the better of it? I was speaking about aeroplanes so we seemed to have wandered.

After School tasks.

In case you get the impression that life was all fun and games it is right that I put the record straight. Not popular these jobs; a boy's idea of life after school, was, run home, throw off the bag and slip out to play with the ball without changing. It never worked. There was the expected shout "Get those good clothes off." It was a sad lesson in the way of life. You could plead that you would take extra care, but you early learned it was a non-starter. Added to this there was the chore of going for buttermilk. I knew the nights as well as my mother. Just try and get out of this by slipping out without her seeing you, would be drawn up sharply with the peremptory command. "Mind this is Hardgatehead night."

Big sister did this till she was promoted to the Forth school. By this time I was age for the soor dook run. It was always a girn, for you had to forego more important issues like playing fitba wi'yir pals. Not only so, the farm was all of two miles from home; nearly at Auchengray station. "See and get a pat of butter in your can" was her parting injunction.

Fortunately other children had the same bother with the same difficult mothers so you were assured of company.

If it was summer and the weather was fair it became quite an adventure. Birds we knew were nesting, and you got quite adept at seeking these out - all the while on the return journey taking care you did not spill any milk. There were convenient peat bogs; great for paddling in. What a mess, although short trousers well rolled up your thighs made it greater fun. Burns were few and in summer carried meagre supplies of water, so you had to know where there was a pond with sufficient clean water for your ablutions. Another point of interest; there was no running water at home. Water from the roof was caught in a barrel at the end of the house. This was suitable for washing clothes, dirty legs, hands and feet, but was unsuitable for cooking.

Every night was the milk run to the Crukens farm; Barries. A pint every morning and evening without fail. The simple thing surely would be to get the two pints in the morning. This argument or suggestion was always met with the response. "It is fresh in the morning and you go after milking at night" No it would not keep through the night, so we were sure of fresh unpasturised milk for the porridge in the morning and a cup before bed.

Why did we feel inferior to the farmers? Was it an inbuilt thing? Fostered and bred in us to know and keep to our station-mining communities were as low as you could get in the social ladder and were expected and indeed told to remember this. Even our parents were not guiltless in this.

Some of our great times were spent with Jimmy Dick - ploughman at the farm with his pair of horses on a wet sleaty winter day and a single furrow plough. Up and down. Soaked to the skin with no modern ideas of protective clothing on allowance for this. A wee laddie on his way home from school falling in along side him and his team, was never made to feel a nuisance; indeed there was always a welcome and a kindly word showing there was an affinity between us, that told of an awareness of kinship. It had something to do with horses and men and laddies with the pride of a straight furrow of turned earth giving a hope of better days and great rewards from soil subjected to the stamp of Clydesdales' feet and steel that wounded; only to produce better in the harvest of autumn.

Then comes the harvest. Hay to be cut and left to dry in our capricious weather, was then turned by hand with a fork before being put into coils of small bundles then into haystacks ready

222

for transport to the farmyard. It rained on many of these summer days and it must have been a worry to the farmer, and extra work for all, if it rained for days. This gives the lie to the myth of constant long days of sunshine.

Then came the summer holidays; if there were no chores to be done at home you rushed through breakfast and up to the farm to give Jimmy a hand to lead out the horses. He never seemed to be out of sorts with us. You knew this especially if he tossed you up on to the back of one of the horses to ride it to the fields. What laddie could not conjure up fantasies of gladiators or Bruce at Bannockburn. From such a vantage point of all the memories of these scenes two events stand out; Dinner back at the farm. You were starving and the soup followed by boiling beef was just the thing to fill you up; but there was something strange going on. The farmer and his family not only ate at a different table but in the kitchen while the ploughman and his helpers ate in the milk house. I would not be more than ten at that time. I could readily see the difference from home. It might have been a case that the big folk were served if there was company but at least you sat at the same table with your pals as long as you obeyed the fundamental rules; hands washed. Mothers could be tiresome and difficult. Worse was when one of the daughters who was in my class at school seemed to feel it beneath her dignity to recognise me. I felt that I was as good as she because she never seemed to beat me at our lessons.

The only parallel to this was to happen at a colliery manager's house some few years later. I had walked a long way to another village in Lanarkshire with my father. We were staying overnight with my aunt and the next day we had been asked to dinner. I was the only child. There were three or four grown up daughters. When the call came to go through to the dining room. I was up like a shot to follow the big folk when one of the daughters stopped me quite abruptly and put me on the right route-first stop the kitchen. To me it was just a scullery.

On the table was a plate, knife and fork, humiliation would have been complete if there had only been a spoon. I had been taught to use cutlery properly from early days. There I had to sit through the meal in isolated loneliness in this crowded room of women onlookers. It must have been the quietest meal I ever ate. Did they resent the trouble they had to take, in providing for me; Was I just to be suffered because their father was in the dining room entertaining? Was I just in the road? One can never tell. Perhaps it was all in my own mind. They never spoke to me, but quietly whispered together. Another thing I felt that day as I thanked them for the meal was anger. My mother would never do that with boys off the street. My anger was fuelled by the fact that the single course was mince and tatties. What a let down; you could get better fare at home any day.

It was certainly far behind the dinners at home or even with Jimmy Dick and never warranted a mention against the sheer joy and lightheartedness of a summer day at the haymaking when a meal was provided at the scene of operations. Food was brought from the farm; scones cheese and fresh milk made a feast for Bert and me and there always seemed to be more than enough. We lay stretched out at the foot of a rick resting our legs and arms as we fuelled up for the rest of the day.

We were not paid in these days, but probably the good dinner and the picnic in the field more than repaid our efforts in the field. Perhaps the company had something to do with the enjoyment. In fairness to the farmer's wife the meals supplied were of a high standard.

The corn harvest would follow later, and again this was governed by the weather and many times the gathering in would

224

stretch well into the autumn and the shawing of the turnips and the howking of the tatties would be held back as the harvest encroached on their time. No gloves were ever worn at any of these tasks and thistles were abundant in the sheaves of corn.

The turnip job was the heaviest of them all for young limbs. You could do this on a Saturday morning. It was well into autumn and winter when this was done using a heuk. You pulled the turnip out of the ground then loped off the tail and the shaw with it.

Chores like going for water meant a trudge down to the 'den with enamelled pails, where there was a plentiful supply of clean spring water that never dried up. It seemed a very long road and up a brae although it was in reality only a half of a mile. We seldom went to the pump in the village; in winter it was often frozen, and in summer it was dry. By the time we left it was non-existent.

The den water never failed; it was not like the burns which dried up quickly in summer, so dooking became a problem. The same thing happened to the rainwater barrel at the end of the house, and water had to be carried for clothes and other washing. Washing was always done on a Tuesday. It was like the law of the Medes and the Persians. You could not put it off-hail rain or snow did not alter the routine; Tuesday was wash day.

One aspect of this was grand; on Monday auntie Kate next door washed and she and our cousins came in for midday tea. It was great fun, a picnic, in the house and there was a big tin of salmon made into sandwiches. We were difficult to fill but greed was frowned upon; if there were overt attempts to get an extra piece, there were two things that mitigated against it. Both mothers were scrupulously fair in their judgment and would soon slap you down if you stepped out of line. By far was the second, worse than the first; you could not get away with deviousness or cheating, with eight to ten pairs of hungry eyes on you.

So on Tuesday the form was changed and we tripped next door and invariably it was corn beef. Far better than eating in your own house. It helped in bonding the two families together. This was a practice that carried on for years and expanded as we grew older, and the two homes became places where hospitality was prodigal and not only for the immediate families; it extended to many others. Could there be some truth in the old saying? 'There is a scattering that tends to increase and a withholding then tends to poverty'. We lived in the days and environment when farmers scattered their seeds-indeed threw it away in view and prospect of an autumn harvest.

One gruesome memory remains of this wash house and the boiler at the back. There was a space between the boiler and the wall. It was warm and hidden, and was useful for hiding seek purposes. It was also the ideal place for producing your first litter of pups. They belonged to two brothers who lived in the old Police Station just across from us. They had a dog and she had her pups in the warmth and security of this little corner behind the boiler. Whither the owner had found out, or my mother had informed him of the fact I knew not. She was going about her works and had reason to go in to the wash house to check if the fire and water were all right when, she saw one of the brothers lifting a sack out of the boiler of boiling water. He had either scalded or drowned the little beasts in it.

I was not there, but on learning this from my mother, and knowing her temperament and her abhorrence of cruelty in any shape or form, I can readily appreciate her reaction; his ears would be ringing and if he had been smaller she might have cuffed his ears and they would have been ringing to a different tune.

226

We were never too happy about the brothers, and although we had never been inside the house we had heard enough stories about the old jail and the gloominess of the whole building. Bigger children and adults as well, had frightened young minds by fearful pictures of being locked in the jail never to get out; victims of bad men who would never let you go. We gave the place a wide berth at all times and after dark it was an eerie haunted barn of a place and as bad as young, frightened minds could make it.

Myths became facts; legends are history and in this case it carried for me, and others as well, an aura of secrecy and mystery with its resulting terror that took a long time to find its true perspective in maturing lives.

One only remaining memory of the men and the house was a sombre one; a day when two black horses with black plumes flying from their heads and drawing a glass coach arrived at the door. Yes death had come to the dreaded prison and although I did not understand much about deaths and funerals there was a certain glow of well being suffusing me as I stood at the door of our home. It was my first view of a funeral and a coffin; indeed it was the only time I can remember seeing horses at one. Relief might be the best way to describe the feeling. Soon after the brother was to move away, and the house was let to another family.

Perhaps the lesson has never been learned. Nothing was known of these men; but the drowning of the wee pups was the perameter in which all other things were judged.

Drowning pups became a common event and became an expected thing in the village where dogs ran freely around the doors and couplings were witnessed. The sight of two dogs apparently stuck together back end to back end raised

227

questions in my mind that were only answered in a very evasive way; but to go back to the earlier events.

It was judgment without trial; conclusion reached without facts being established; decisions made without validity. Even the assurance that the old men were lonely and friendless, not doing any harm, failed to allay the fears; so imagination took over and to go out at night near the house in the dark was a nightmare not to be experienced alone, but only if accompanied by a big sister. This of course, in spite of the fact she was probably the cause of fear in the first place, with her stories of dark deeds and fearful happenings.

By this time demolition of the village had begun and empty and broken down rows of houses were daily evidence of a thriving community in its death throws. Fewer people were abroad at night and lit windows with paraffin lamps casting light on the blinds were diminishing rapidly.

CHAPTER 20

BANSHEES

Winter has great memories; frosty days and word going the rounds; the ponds are bearing, or even the overflow from the pump that ran down the hill, unless the pump was frozen. Even the sheughs with a layer of ice was sufficient to cause jubilation. Just made for tackety boots. We never owned skates and I never remember seeing a pair in the early years. It had to take a move to Wilsontown that saw such sophistication of shows on ice with skates and these too were very limited to a few and were of infrequent use.

One frosty event remains vivid still. It was Saturday. Miners finished early; there was no school and the next day being Sunday meant a long lie. We children had spent the day nearer home where ice was available. This night after dark the big ones going further afield to large ponds; Bobby and Johnny Tennant and my cousin John were the leaders. All were grown up so this was a chance not to be missed, for you would not be allowed to go so far away after the shadows lengthened and finally gave up to darkness with a star studded sky. With big ones you would be safe enough so they kept assuring us. There were four girls all five years older; they added to a crowd of eager boys made up the party plus Mamie Brown-my age. She never missed any of our exploits. Even at football she was always picked in a side but was strictly forbidden to play anywhere but in goals.

On this occasion we had an addition to our gang; Jim Little from the Railway cottages on the Haywood and Auchengray line. To get to his home you had to pass Clark's Walls. We knew the old dilapidated farm as 'The Den', and it was opposite one of the many bings left as spoil from a past age. It was a spot we visited regularly every day for water but never after dark. He was seldom with us and never after daylight had gone.

He had been up playing with us in the early part of the day and was just leaving for home when this excursion was proposed. He was invited to join us with the assurance that he would be seen home. So we set off over the moors to a pond larger than the ones nearer home, in high spirits. What an adventure this was to us, in the company of men who were not always amenable to childrens' presence. "You're too wee' was their general response to any pleas.

You hid any fear of the dark; you would never admit it, or your dispatch home would be swift and irreversible, so we enjoyed the trek taking in all the frozen peat bogs and ponds on our way. At first, time did not matter in the excitement and enjoyment, but as darkness deepened there was a feeling among the younger members that it was time for home and bed and I could be counted in the number. We would not go back alone in the dark so we had to wait the pleasure of the adults. They were in no hurry, we had to stay. You could not see the friendly lights in the windows from this lonely moor.

Fear has a way of building up in young minds, and by the time the older ones were ready to go home, we were terrified by the dark, the distance home, and the stories they told us. The least sound was further cause for terror. Then there was talk of 'Banshees' and what would happen if they caught you out on the moor at night. Unknown, as we were leaving the place of laughter and fun, that had developed into a pit of blackness two

230

of the older men had slipped away in the darkness away to the right and the other to the left. Among the number and the moonless night none of us had missed them. As we trudged home keeping close for safety the teller of tales was interrupted by the wailing on one side. Banshee Banshee in a long drawn out tone. As this stopped it was taken up on the other flank. It must have been the first time my hair stood on end. It was indeed a terrified group of a dozen who crowded closely together, fearful of breaking out from the safety of the herd and running for home.

The lights of home appeared, and with the vision there was a cessation of the awful noise and the story teller became quiet as well. There was a sudden rush for home with its safety, light and warmth, when in a frightened voice Jim shouted "Whit aboot me. Ah'm no gaun doon by the den on ma ain. Somebody wull need to come home wi me."

No one seemed inclined to take him up on his cry of despair, and all dispersed to their own homes and left three; Jim Jean and I to do what we liked; it was none of their business. We had just round the corner of the house to go, and when the rest had gone. She said "Dinnae be feert we'll tak yi hame." Quickly I squealed out "Ahm no guan, its awright for him he'll hae company richt to his hoose, and even so you, and him, are bigger than me; you'll jist run awa frae me and I'll get coat. Onywae there will be me and you, oor Jean, comin hame and it is up the brae aa the wey."

"Ah'll tak your haun aa the wey and a'll no run awa." So we set off down the hill towards Jim's house along the narrow track between the bing and the Den. It was a different place from the daylight one we visited every day for water at the well.

It was different even from the crowd in the dark on the moor; but there was still three of us as we hurried past-no

231

thought of a drink of this well tonight. There was no sound of talking but ears skinned for any little noise. There would be no little noises because fear had magnified everything, so dimly discerned shapes in the steading, became phantoms ready to pounce; even the heavy breathing of cattle or the ordinary sound of a sheep moving nearbye lent wings to our feet, and soon the other two were racing me to the railway cottages down by the line to Auchengray. Then we were at his door and with a hurried 'cheerio' the door opened and he was gone.

But what of the brave ones who had to face the darkness and the 'den' and the dreaded brae to get home. Everyone, even the victim, home and dry, while the exception; a daft big sister and a wee frightened laddie were left to brave the horrors of the long road home.

"I think we'll just run past this time," suggested Jean. "Na yi'll take tae yir heels and leave me staunin and ah'm feart." Later on she was to tell me. "Ah could hardly keep up with you."

Yes we were country born no street lights and plenty of empty houses, but still susceptible to suggestions of things beyond our ken. The one who comes out of this night's events, dramatic and fearful, with any credit was Jean. I can say without fear of contradiction that her attitude was always to side with the underdog and the weak. It is all in the process of growing up and past happening have little meaning if forgotten, but life is surely made of scenes and experiences like these.

Bullfighters?

No night scene, but daytime and summer at that. The time-1926 strike-when men were idle and children had long summer holidays from school.

We had all been playing at our usual pursuits, and had gone

232

indoors to see if we could wangle a piece of jeely to keep us going till dinner time. As usual father was out. Normally this did not matter; children all the world over do not shout for father, but echoing down through the years and heard still, is the call, "Where's my mother." She was the citadel to which we gravitated for comfort of a handy apron to dry tears; listen to a tale of woe, on the scoring of a wonder goal with a tuppeny ba. We were privileged to know, if she was not in, she would not be far away. No latch key kids in these days.

This was a beautiful summer morning of which there seemed to be no lack- a surfeit of these during this long miner's strike. On being questioned about father's whereabouts: he could have been a number of places; digging for coal at the Crusher bing. Lifting sleepers on the old Lawhead railway, or out walking with the other men; she assured us he had gone for a walk up to Mountainblow Farm.

With this information Jean and I set off over by No.8 row and up through the fields in the direction of the farm. It was a fair distance for a six year old; up hill all the way, our desti-nation; with Skylaw, this was the highest point in the surrounding farmland. How far we got I cannot say, but there was an old pit bing near the top and we climbed to the top to get a view towards the farm. There was a sudden squeal from the leader of the expedition. "There's a bull." And turning she set off at breakneck speed. Luckily she grabbed my hand and off we went down the bing and on to the grassy field towards a fence. We would never make it, and I was terrified. To this day I cannot remember if there was a bull or not, but I certainly knew the decision was not mine. I seemed to be oftener on my knees than my feet, but still she hauled me along and at last we threw ourselves through the fence, but this was not the end of this record breaking run. Even the fence with its measure of safety did not cause any slackening of speed, for terror lent wings to our feet that morning; it was a pair of frightened children who reached the familiar rows of the village.

The explanation for us not finding the men was simple. They had changed their minds as to the direction of their walk, and were quite unaffected by our childish rage, and laughed us to scorn, as if there never was a bull and we had imagined the whole thing. It took mother some time to settle us down after a row with my father.

One last anecdote about frights and darkness. We never had running water in or around the house so sanitary arrangements were simple and elementary.

Each row of houses had a midden with its attendant dry closet (Shunky.) In our case it was situated right round the other side of our home immediately against the open fields. It was all right in the daytime, but when you were a wee laddie night time is a different story. It was then you needed your big sister to go with you. Sometimes the moon would be shining brightly and even in its absence the stairs had their inbuilt illumination. The absence of lights outside made the stars shine all the better, but clouds could effectually cancel this out.

There was always a bit of grumbling when nature called, and you had to be accompanied to the closet. Big sister would stand outside, and she had to leave the door open. There were the usual questions made at frequent intervals flung from the wee hoose "Are ye still there." And the grumbling retort. "Ahm no staunin here aa nicht. If ye dinnae hurry up ahm awa into the hoose." She never did up till this night. It is clearly etched on my memory, and the threat did materialise and she did run away, but only round the corner at the back door.

She had previously planned the whole escapade, and had an old white sheet hidden for this purpose, and when she ran away she had grabbed this sheet and flung it over herself. She had not long to wait; this wee boy was making even timeround from the shunky with his trousers held up-no time to fix braces in his flight and fright. Worse was to come. As I rounded the corner of the house this apparition leapt out on me and I collapsed in a heap at her feet. Jean's remorse and her fear of the effects made her shout for mother. For her sake it was not the best thing she could have done, because father, as well as mother rushed out at the cries of distress. I had passed out, but she was not passed by. A hot bottom ensured that. The cure must have been effective for there were never any recurrences of this caper again for any of us. She said later on "I thocht ye were deid." This was the only time in my life I ever knew her to be unkind to me.

Frights in these circumstances and these nights were of the imagination. It may well be a potent force in young lives.

There were other things that frighten, that were not just imagination but real and menancing; like the Sunday we were all coming home from the Sunday School which was held in the Hawthorn Hall in Wilsontown (Bell Gibson's Hall.) It was a summer day so clothes were at a minimum; no coats scarfs or bunnets, but light dresses and good suits. We had just come down through Rootpark-Fues-and on to Sanny Somerville's field just beyond the farm. The sky suddenly darkened and the rain come down in sheets with its accompanying thunder and lightening.

We were at least a mile from home and all were terrified. It was a fearsome storm. Not only so but our home lay down through Sanny's field and past the crusher bing. There were lots of fences to be negotiated and everybody knew that lighting could strike off wires and you could be killed. The fences were too high to jump and the spaces between the taut wires meant you had to squeeze through. You could catch your jacket buttons if you were in a hurry. Had we not proved this on many occasions when racing each other home on other days?

All this fear, added to the misery of being soaked to the skin, was a nightmare that had to be endured, till we were in the safety of home. Tiredness never came into it; and big and small limbs did speeds that could not be bettered at the annual trip. The last fence was cleared and home beckoned as never before. Comfort, dry clothes, and a place at the tea table furthest away from the window, for did you not know, that to sit at the window was a very dangerous thing to do, in a thunderstorm.

Perhaps the most lasting memory of storms was the great gale of January 1929. The wind had been blowing hard all week and by Thursday of that week it had reached storm force. The workman's train came from Auchengray to Haywood and then on to Wilsontown around six o'clock in the morning. Most of the miners took this train and then walked either to Climpy owned by Coltness Coal Company to Dixon's pit owned by Wm. Dixon-the famous name associated with 'Dixon's Bleezes at Glasgow.

A few miners walked to their work and the shortest way was by the railway. One of these miners was Tom Geddes. His son Robert was in my class at the school. The family lived at the Stone Row. He had taken the railway that stormy morning and because of the strong winds, he had not heard the train coming along the line behind him and was killed.

The storm raged on still further and by Friday afternoon had reached its peak. At school we had one of these infrequent occasions, when we were given a half day, to get home before the storm got any worse. Our glee at this relief from school was short lived. Half days for heavy rain or snow were more than welcome. Many were the anxious glances out of the window. Debate at play time would invariable centre on the weather, as we spent our brief respite from lessons in a classroom; empty because of depleted school roll. Anything would be better than Auld Jean Lambie's skule but this was to have a different ending.

No rain; just wind that could blow you over; glad to get home out of the storm for tea round the coal fire. The rest of the day was a catalogue of disasters. As described earlier there was a wooden structure with a corrugated roof. This covered the doors into the respective houses, so the entrance into each of the kitchens was by a side door at each side of this scullery. A wood partition divided this part into two with an outside door for each compartment. Each of these had only a skylight.

The first step to fear and confusion happened when Auntie Kate's kitchen window blew in so all the weans decamped round the corner to the safety of our kitchen. For us this was a great adventure. There was safety in numbers and there was a real big crowd.

Our respite was short lived for the next thing that fell prey to the fierce wind was the door into the Scullery facing the south west storm. It did not take the wind long to negotiate the space made through the blown away door. There ensued an unequal struggle between a flimsy partition, and a wind that seemed to rejoice in its supremacy, so with a roar of collapsing wood the partition gave up the unequal struggle and crashed into our Scullery; fortunately it did not block the entrance into it, or better, an exit to the outside world.

Gone was the feeling of security and when the skylight was ripped off the roof of the remaining Scullery terror reigned supreme in the one occupied room in the house. No men were in the house. In fact the storm had passed, by the time they came off the four o'clock train. Long before that, the glory of this half day had evaporated.

Coal fires were the order of the day, and needed renewing after the last pailful in the Scullery had been used. Despite pleadings my mother insisted she would need to get more coal. Did no your father need hot water to wash in? And it was time the tatties were on for his dinner, and the others coming in tired and dirty from the pit.

Pleading on my part for her not to out out, became a wail of despair when she stated she was going out. She did just that; having difficulty in opening the door against the wind and slammed shut as she edged through. I knew were the coalhouse was situated; round the side of the house and against it. It too had a corrugated roof. She managed to get a pail filled and brought it in; despite greeting weans trying to restrain her, but in vain. She had to go. Just as the pleading was at its loudest there was a great noise above the raging hurricane. It was on the outside. Most of us were so frightened that we were sure the house was blowing away. No amount of weeping and wailing made any difference and when she struggled back in with the filled pail, and the news, that the noise we had heard was a chimney can from the top of our two storied house, crashing through the roof of the coal house. That was the end. She must not go out till father came home.

But that was not the last call of duty for her, this horrible day; there was a knock on the only surviving door in the house and Bob Tennant, who lived on the leaward side of this rubbish of a building shouted in, that Harry the Co. Baker was down at the Square. We did not care very much for him; he was the school attendance officer. To us he was quite a fearsome character and if you were off with childish ailments like measles or mumps you were afraid to go out during convales-

238

cence in case he saw you and reported you to the school authorities, so this long standing grudge added to the general appeal.
"Let him go himself; he can surely bring up all the bread for us
all-the fact that there were other five in our family to be fed
over the weekend and I think about twelve next door did not
count. The baker only came to the village twice per week.

Mother reached once more for her coat, and off she went
down the brae to the van. Nobody went with her, if I remember
correctly. It was a relief to see her back safe and sound with her
apron filled with bread, and in her pocket there was slipped a
cake of bluebird toffee. This was our family treat every Friday
and was a welcome addition to our Friday penny. Perhaps
someone may be upset about the mode of carrying food in your
apron because it was not a dainty delicate thing with frills round
the edges. Do not worry. Although made from course material it
was always a clean one for this task. The relief by all when the
men came trooping in with dirty faces to wash and be fed in this
single end, brought a measure of normality to the experience.

During the night it snowed and I can remember two things;
snow lying on the Scullery floor underneath the hole in the roof
where the skylight window had been, and going out with my
sledge after breakfast. Later on my father showed me a large
crack in the gable end of the house, so the storm had been severe
enough to damage the structure of the main part of the building.

I never felt very comfortable about this house again.
Especially at bedtime when we went up to bed, and lay and
listened to the moaning of the wind. It did not take long for me
to seek the refuge of the set-in-bed where mother and father
slept. I think father objected quite strongly about this
arrangement, and I was soon made aware that wee laddies did
not sleep at the bottom of their parents beds. I can now appreciate why father did not think this was a suitable arrangement;

239

at the time it was safe there, and not away up in the roof with only a skylight window. This whole event just added the finishing touch to the terror experienced when Bob Tennant died with cancer, and I could not sleep for his cries of anguish and pain heard plainly through the wall.

On a lighter note there comes back to me a summer scene and again, Bert, my cousin, and best pal was involved. We speak in our older years of past times and events and undoubtedly nostalgia leads to exaggeration and distance timewise as well as geographical lends enchantment.

It was a fine sunny day; whither it was a lasting heatwave of a few weeks or just a day or two I cannot recall. It may just have been a singularly fine day, admist a priority of wet dull ones. We at least were dressed for the summer; old short trousers-note-not into the modern trend of dressing up in men's apparel-with no stockings or boots. It was a joy to get out without a home knitted jersey with its turned down collar. Oh! The freedom of a sleeveless shirt; what a change. The jersey was made of coarse worsted and, for school I always wore a home knitted tie. It was jaggy and this was compounded if you had a haircut and the hairs stuck inside the collar. It seemed to take ages for the hairs to disappear and there were frequent calls for Mother to blow down your neck to get rid of the harvest of father's No 1 clippers.

Most boys did not wear ties, but it seemed to be the rule in our home that boys should wear a tie to school. No uniform at the Hi'wid but this was probably a form of snobbery, which went under the title of being Mair respectable! I do not know, but one thing I do remember, at the end of the last lesson it was hauled off and shoved into the pocket and you were doubly free; from the incarceration behind a desk since nine o'clock, and from the restriction of extra clothing that was only a nuisance and an irritation. What use was a jersey or a tie if you were going to

240

score more goals this week than last during the morning and afternoon short breaks, and the longer interval at dinner time. Food was secondary to the real reason for living-football. It was a quick snatch at a couple of slices of bread with butter and jam washed down with hot tea in a tin flask that had been simmering on the top of the coal stove in the classroom. Many of the pupils lived a good distance from the school and it was necessary to bring a piece. If the weather was fine there was the playground and the fields beyond. If not you could sit around the warm stove and eat you piece in comfort or play in one of the old classrooms.

Many of us, although living nearer the school did this as often as it was allowed. Back to this summers' day. We had an old bike; it was a communal affair built by some of the older men for us to learn to go a bike. I would hate to give the impression that this was a gleaming model like B.S.A. Not at all; it was not self motivated; neither was it made to go by the effort of the cyclist. It was gravity controlled and could not go unless it was on an incline and only could go one way-downhill. The same principle obtained when you reached the bottom or hit an obstacle on the way, you still went down by the simple expedient of falling off:

The machine if such it could be called was a basic model no Mark II - nothing fancy. It comprised on old bike frame, rescued from its last expected resting place in some old corner. They were not actually thick on the ground; although most houses in the village, where there were working men, usually had a bike. Nevertheless they were built to last, like everything in those, now seeming far off days, and were not discarded until they were literally run into the ground.

The frame had no seat; an old tattie bag fulfilled that purpose. It did not have gears, brakes or bell. There was no chain or sprocket or pedals to drive it. The wheels had no tyres

241

or tubes and it did not matter if some of the spokes were missing. It needed a pair of handle bars and you were ready for the off.

The village was adapted to this means of transport being quite hilly so we did not lack for circuits to hone our skills; the greatest of these was the ability to stay on for the journey and learn to fall off when the machine ran out of steam on the level. The whole experience was built on competition; to see who could go the fastest and the furthest. For this you needed a hefty push at the top and if someone went further than you had managed there was the invariable argument. "You got a better push than I did. It's no fair."

There were three main slopes; one at the top of the Planting coming over the hill from the station and zooming down to the 'Iron Brig'.

Another was down the Plough (Ploo) on the same hill on a path to the west side of the village and finishing on the old Lawhead railway.

The third and this is the one on which this incident took place, was the main street of the village and like the first one mentioned finished at the Iron Brig. It started practically up at our house. While the previous tracks were mainly composed of grass this was the remains of the rough road still used by carts and vans. It never had been tarred-Macadam had not reached our village and indeed has never laid a roller on this. In addition many of the houses were empty and demolition was being carried out by Bruce Thomson, and his sons who lived in the big house near the station.

If you got a real good push you could go right down to the Brig and even down to the wooden bridge that carried the railway from Auchengray to Wilsontown. It was still in operation at this time just before you reached the Co.

242

Having stressed earlier that this was a communal affair, by its very nature it was used mostly by those who built it, or the bigger ones. During school holidays the men would be working at the pit so it gave the wee yins a chance. Bert and I had acquired it this morning and were have great fun. Chanceys each was never a problem with us. We were fair to each other.

It was Bert's turn and I gave him a heft push and away he sailed, I following on the rough road, both of us yelling at the top of our voices.

But there was an enemy at the bottom, planning Bert's downfall, in the form of another boy intent on fun at our expense. His name was Willie Thomson. As Bert went sailing past he rushed out and pushed Bert off the bike. Fortunately he did not fall on the hard road. In fact he had a soft landing, among a clump of nettles.

The cries of glee had changed in seconds, to a shout of fright, followed by bellows of anguish and anger, as Bert leapt up and away after the perpetration of this foul act. His cries could be heard as he pursued "I'll murder yi if ah catch yi ah'll murder yi." I thought at the time it might have come true if he had caught him but Nungy had a good start and reached the safety of his home before Bert could catch him. When he came back he was a mass of blisters and it took both of us a long time to get him eased of the pain by the application of dock leaves, a tried and trusty remedy. Perhaps there is a moral in this. Wherever there are nettles, nature invariably provides docks nearby.

CHAPTER 21

THREE HALF CROWNS

The story falls mainly in the latter part of the nineteen twenties and early thirties in two small villages of the Upperward of Lanarkshire, Haywood and Wilsontown. By this time the boom of the late nineteenth century and the beginning if the twentieth had collapsed in the former place, as it had done at Wilsontown a hundred years previously when the Iron Works had closed there. This was a time of special hardship, as depicted by the Rev.Jas Walker in 1830.

The once thriving works with its furnaces, forges, rolling mills and shops of smiths, carpenters, engineers and millwrights, which in 1807-8 supported 2000 souls did finally close in 1812: the population turned adrift in the world. The closing of the works had a dreadful effect on this part, but far worse through the parish. The market was closed to farmers etc. Throughout the area and many were reduced to beggary.

Fortunately the presence of high quality coal revived the prospects of Wilsontown, but in the end hastened the demise of Haywood.

Many pits and small mines had been worked in the area, and in the Lanarkshire OS 6" sheet xx1857 there were shown to be seventeen disused pits in and around the village. By 1920 Haywood was finished as a place of high employment; the only

244

real work left was at Dixon's pit at Wilsontown and Climpy owned by Coltness Iron Company.

The part of the village mostly affected was the area containing seventeen rows of brick built houses, made up of single ends, room and kitchens. There were approximately two hundred and fifty homes. This must have represented a fair population.

The place is a ghost of its former hustle and bustle after the general strike of 1926. No pits now working, and only one or two small mines were operating, and the manpower travelling to pits further afield at Dixon's and Climpy. The population migrated up to Forth and Wilsontown as houses became available. Only a few remained at the commencement of the events.

The industrial life of the village was encompassed in a few decades at the end of the century, and little more than two at the start of the next.

By the time of the incidents recorded, only the periphery of the place remained; the heart finally torn out of it by the demolition by Bruce Thomson, who lived in the big house next to the station. In this area seventeen rows of brick built houses were occupied by two hundred and fifty families, and with an average of five to a home, must have held at least twelve hundred and fifty people.

The village as a viable industrial entity was finally laid to rest after the General Strike of 1926, and only its ghost remained. No pits were working and only a few small mines were left, while the manpower travelled further a field to Climpy and Dixon's pits. This inevitably led to the migration of the population to Forth, as houses became available.

Two of the buildings left standing were up at the highest part of the village, and consisted of a licensed grocer, and a two storied house with three families. In these the boys involved lived; Alex at the shop and Bob and Bert in the other place. They were cousins. They were also sons in mining families, where money was hardly earned and was just as wisely and frugally spent. Their parents were members of the Gospel Hall nearby, and to them the rearing of children was a sacred trust; honesty was something that was practised by them and taught to their young folks. They were not much concerned about the Gold Standard; more about the value of copper-pennies and halfpennies. They were scarce and the contents of purses were limited.

Things must be rationally examined. In Bob's case there was only one wage earner; a roof had to be kept over the family, so the rent had to be paid. Then there was the Co. Book, so it was allocated its share of the weekly budget. In this type of economy a threepenny was a lot of money, and to think of taking one out of you mother's purse was never contemplated. Even a halfpenny was never considered, and from a boy's point of view was always understood in the light of pocket money; the Friday penny. It was a fortune that was never known, to vary.

With Alex it was different. As far as Bob could judge, all Alex wanted, Alex got, and not only so there was a till that he could visit when his mother was in the house. To Bob's knowledge, only on two occasions did this ever happen, and a half crown was involved both times.

It was a Saturday morning during a spell of real wintry weather. Snow lay thick and frost had made it crunchy for walking. The sky was clear, and the weak sun shed its little warmth and light on the moors all around. The ponds out there in the whiteness were bearing: it was a day for sliding with solid tackety boots to keep your feet dry and warm, as well as taking you whizzing over the ice on one foot, or crouched down on your hunkers, seeing who could go fastest and furthest without falling.

Alex called for Bob and asked him to go for a walk. Alex explained his plan, as he produced the half crown he had taken from the till. "Don't tell Bert when you gie him a shout, but ah'll kid oan ah've fun it in the snaw, an ken whit; We'll go tae Auchengray tae the wee shop at the station, and we'll come hame in the train." This promised to be some day and some adventure with a whole half crown.

They had not gone far when Alex rushed forward and shoved his hand down through the snow and came up to show his find. By this time Bob was getting over his qualms of conscience, and his uneasiness was rapidly dispensing at the prospect of sweeties and a penny pop, plus a hurl in the train all by themselves without big folk to bother them. Not only so, but it was not he who had taken the money, therefore he could not be blamed. Whither Bert had been taken in by our pal's sleight of hand he never found out till later on when Bert said, "Ye shirly think ah'm daft."

Notwithstanding his original fears and reservations, they had a great day; indeed the adventure seems to be enhanced by the very fact that it was against all the rules he was accustomed to follow, and of course the rewards were great. Awee lee at the end of the day would surely be a fair answer "Jist ower the muirs sliding", to his mother's question whenever he went in the door. "Whaur hae ye been stravaiging aa day."

The second incident had a different sequel; Bert was not here on that occasion.

Hall Thomson had a paper shop at Loan Street, better known to the locals as No.8 row. He also stocked sweets and a variety of soft drinks. One Autumn Alex asked him to go to Hall's since he had a half crown to spend. He was easy meat for a suggestion like that; he was crime hardened by this time. Was this not his second attempt at this lucrative way of living? He had still to learn that crimes does not pay.

On the way over from Greenbank Alex confided that a few days earlier he had been in the shop with a half crown, and it would look very suspicious if he went in with another one so soon. Persuasive as ever he convinced Bob it would be all right for him to go in. Nobody would suspect anything, and so the challenge was taken up and in he marched as bold as he could.

Who was serving but Hall himself, and in answer to his query "What do you want"? He placed his fortune on the counter, and asked for ogo-pogo eyes-real favourites with all the children- they lasted for ages and turned all different colours as you sucked them. Caramels were in the equation as well as candy, but he never got round to asking for them. The man on the right side of the counter hesitated for a moment then brusquely asked "Where did you get this kind of money?" Quickly he replied. "Ah fun it doon the raw." An answer like that might be acceptable today; in that time it was unthinkable. If such a sum had indeed been lost, everyone would have known. The logical outcome would have incorporated a search party of all the able bodied members of the community, and the finding second only to the great story in the Gospel of St Luke in the good old Book.

Added to all this was the stonewall fact that the shopkeeper would know that Bob's family had not that kind of money to throw away on sweeties. Was this not the shop where he spent his Friday penny, deliberating at the window, and also in the
248

shop the best value for his weekly riches? Hall's final words were terse and to the point. " I don't know where you got it but you are not spending it in this shop. Forbye that, I'll be seeing your father about this."

This he duly did that same night when he called at the house, and gave his father the gruesome details. It was a chastened and crest fallen laddie that went to bed that night. The belt was not often used in the home, but the punishment must have fitted the crime. It never happened again: maybe it was better to learn early and dearly that 'Crime does not pay'. How simple and stupid he must have been to think, that in the straitened circumstances of his daily life in the great depression years, he would get away with such a felony.

The third half crown is a different story altogether, with an ending as choice as its beginning.

No irate father or indignant wise shopkeeper just an old irascible doctor who terrified you if you had to go to the surgery for medicine; even more fearful if it fell to your lot to call on a Saturday night at the Welfare at Forth to ask him to leave his game and his buddies to visit someone at home.

His waiting room, a wooden and glass appendage stuck on to the end of his house, was narrow, cold and meagrely furnished. A wooden bench holding eight or nine people was against the wall opposite the door into the surgery and the aperture on bole through which he dispensed medicines. Long memories recall the famous pink bottles, an unfailing remedy for all childhood ailments. The final indignity was the bole-hole. There was a small wooden platform on which you stood if you just wanted a bottle, but you had to be a reasonable height to manage this. If you were little of stature, and of a nervous disposition the whole thing was a nightmare.

249

At your back was a form filled with old folks, with others crowded in an around the floor space at the door. To a wee laddie they were as big a menace as the doctor himself as you waited your turn which eventually came when you heard a peremptory shout from inside. "Next." Up you jumped on to the box, and here your misery was compounded; You stood on your tiptoes even clutching the bottom of the bole to raise yourself sufficiently to peer over the edge and number "Could I get my father's medicine." If this was not working, and only the top of your head was showing he would issue a further command. "Speak up I cannot hear you." You might oblige by raising your voice a squeak or two, and from the crowded room would come the ultimate humiliation. "Wull ah gie yi' a docky up, wee yin." And immediately behind this riposte would come the dreaded invitation. "Come into the surgery," and in you would go to be met by a man beaming all over at your discomfort, then in a minute out to face the amusement and comments of the colliers.

He and Nurse Cunningham with the maid, would have made a half back line, the Wanderers would have been proud of any Saturday at Highdyke.

On now to another half crown to show another side to the doctor. It took place when the family had moved to Wilsontown and Bob was twelve. It was a beautiful day during the summer holidays, and he was out walking with his father, who was recovering from a serious illness, and part of his convalescence was walking every day. This was no hardship for him, and of course it was a joy to his son who invariably accompanied him with destinations like Woolfords, Tarbrax Carnwath or Auchengray.

This day it was agreed that they try Bathgate for a change. He was vaguely familiar with the other places, but he had never been the length of this strange town; but if his father said it, that was good enough for him. How he enjoyed these outings; no hardship or tiredness ever diminished his joy in these adventures. Indeed his love of the outdoors was born, in early years of field and moor, out of his father's enthusiasm, and his ability to talk with a boy thirty five years his junior as an equal and make him feel it.

They had gone up the West Calder road as far as the finger post at the top of Briech Braes, when Dr Reid drew up in his car. No sounding of his horn, or a wave in passing but an open window with a greeting from the occupant. "Where are you gong today Matha", and his father's ready response. "The laddie and I are taking a bit walk to Bathgate."
"Jump in then I'm going to Polkement pit, but I have a call at Fauldhouse first; You can get off at the crossroads for Stoneyburn and Fauldhouse and walk up to Longridge and if you are there when I come back there you will get down to Polkement.

There was no possibility of them missing another hurl in the Doctor's car if his wee legs could carry him up the brae. Why did he have to worry? The car was waiting for them when they arrived, and in he hopped again.
What a day this was turning out to be, getting two lifts in the doctor's car was something special. Not many laddies got one hurl.

The car drew up at the road end, and they got out. Now to the climax of this wonderful day. As he left the car the doctor whispered. "That will get you and your father an ice cream slider when you get to Bathgate" and slipped a coin into his hand: it was a half crown. Bob was overcome and could only murmur his thanks, but his stuttering words allied to his father's gratitude, must have made the doctor's day as they waved him away.

"Ah'm no spendin aa that money, oan ice cream", he declared. "Let's hae oor tea in Bathgate", which they did and he paid for it.

Some of the doctor's generosity was rubbing of on a wee laddie of twelve and shortened the miles uphill and down.

This is the story of the half crown that made three people happy.

CHAPTER 22

A STRANGER'S RETURN

The phone rang; I noted the time. It was 9.30 p.m as I lifted the receiver and gave my number. The voice was feminine, strange but familiar although it was two years since I heard it. We had corresponded over the intervening period.

"Guess who is on the phone?" I searched my memory, and suddenly I knew. "It's Elizabeth from New Zealand, but why are you phoning at this time?. It will be the middle of the night. Can't you sleep? It is either a bad conscience, or you have had too big a supper." She soon put that right. "It is not the middle of the night. I have just heard the nine o'clock news on the television."

"You can't be in Britain; it is only two years since you were here. You must be made of money."

"I am, another guess. I am in Scotland." My incredulity increased when she went on to say." I'm in Edinburgh like the last time. I am only on a flying visit but I'm not alone this time." She had me listening now, "Another girl friend"? I asked.

"Nothing like that. My boy friend is with me." I quickly broke in "Is he from Scotland?"

"No he is not; but he has, like myself ancestors who were born here." In answer to my next query she was quick to put me in the picture.

"When I came last time, at least we went about together. He was a bit upset then I was away so long. I was hoping for an advancement in our relationship, and I feel that parting and my stay, must have made up his mind that he would need to do something about it."

"He was a fool to let you tour the world on your own. You must tell me all about it." We agreed that she should bring this wonderful man to see me the next day.

They arrived in time for coffee; I had tea. As I opened the door I was impressed when I saw them. She was still the beautiful stranger at the monument; he was an upstanding young man. They did complement each other.

During the tea break it became clear that he did not talk as freely a she did. I was to say to them later. "No wonder he is quiet he can't get a word in edgeways." Nevertheless, the formality that was felt at the beginning soon vanished, as he was brought more and more into the conversation. I was glad for her especially as she whispered to me. "He was my boyfriend; his is now my husband. I had to do something to prevent this big kind man from escaping. Mind you; he did not make much attempt at fleeing."

"What are you two whispering about?" "Nothing, we both replied. She went on to say "Allan, tell him about our visit." He did.

"Our honeymoon is a gift from both our parents. I felt that we must see this wonderful land-according to Elizabeth and my parents who had been here thirty years previously. There is something timeless about coming back to your roots. Coming here was her suggestion; my links are further north. They lie in Aberdeenshire. We are on our way there, but we had to stop in

254

Edinburgh; it would never do to be in Scotland without stopping in the capital of Scotland."

That was just an excuse; her talk the over holiday has been. "You must see Haywood." Did I say he could not talk; he was proving me wrong. What are your plans? When do you contemplate visiting?

She was quick to respond. "Whenever it suits you and the weather is right." So we fixed to spend the next day-Wednesday-if the weather was fine.

It was agreed that he would take his car and would call for me. He had hired a car and was keen to improve his driving in and around Edinburgh. I arranged to take them a different route than these taken before, taking in Carnwath. So we headed out of the town by way of the 'Long Whang.' There we stopped for lunch at the 'Wee Bush' with its inscription announcing 'Better a wee bush than nae shield.' (Shelter). She was not inclined to leave it at that when I mentioned the cemetery.
"Perhaps I would know some of the names; at least I could take some details that might interest my folks."

Again it was into the car and off to Forth via Stobwood, and the ford at the Miller's burn. We did not linger there apart from a glimpse of the houses where many of the tenants from Haywood at the slum clearance were housed. We proceeded to Wilsontown to view the remains of the ill fated iron works and look at the place where the Big House had been; down which steps the bankrupt owner went with no possessions left, apart from the clothes he wore.

She seemed more concerned about the churchyard and any information she could glean. Alan; all this time had the

255

bemused look of a stranger in a strange land. Showed signs that we were on more familiar ground when she said "This is the road that man brought me in his car; remember that rascal that charged me thirty pounds for my first trip."

At this time she decided to take over as chief guide. "Let me tell Alan all about the rest. You can correct me if I forget something or make a mistake. Tashyburn was still occupied as was the mine cottage. Coming to the school she stopped. "There are the pillars of the boys' and girls' playground. My granny attended it and so did our guide." Thereafter she was in her element, regularly consulting her note book. I let her wander about and soon the camera was out again.

I left them and went up once more to our vantage point on a previous visit. I sat down, not at the war memorial-it had been removed and positioned down where the old Cooperative and the miners 'welfare' had stood. Soon they joined me but there was a disappointed look in her face.

"Why have they shifted it and placed it in a new position? Was it not better where it was?" There seemed to be something symbolic about a monument to brave men on a hillside. Where it is now? It is quite insignificant." I agreed. "It was thought it would be easier of access in the new position, and not stuck up where cars could not go." Cars could go up here; there is evidence. See the old Austin. It certainly will never be moved even if there was a road. It will be its own epitaph.

It had been a splendid day, but still she was not finished, as she pointed out to her husband the range of the Pentlands and the surrounding villages. The next statement was more of a question.

"Let us take Allan over the old road to the little inn and

have one of their toasted sandwiches. They were good."

We did just that, and after a busy and enjoyable day, it was back to the city of Edinburgh.

I was to make another and last visit.

So I stood where the stranger stood; at the same high point. But there is a difference this morning. Previously I had company; now I stood alone. On the earlier occasion it had been a beautiful day of sunshine and blue skies; now it was raining, blacking out with a grey mist, the fair aspect of the Pentland Hills and right round, the Biggar Hills and on to Tinto. My only consolation - they were still there. You don't move mountains overnight. There is no wind, just a dark dreich day, in a drab dull environment.

The grass and threshes of this wilderness, shed their own tears of sympathy in response to the grief of the clouds. Was this the place that I eulogized? This grim, barren, featureless place was the haunt of ghosts and silence; not of solace, but of sadness.

Nevertheless the harshness and been smoothed over the years, and it is true that much is hidden that was ugly before. Memories lie buried, not just in my mind, but under a canopy of grass rough enough in texture to hide the story of ordinary folk. They never saw the end of their labours.

Was God telling me something? He was not forgetting the past; simply hiding the shame of it from us, while retaining for Himself the secrets of all, till he reveals it in His own good time. Is this the end of my adventure-tears at the withdrawal of the sun? Surely there must be some brightness. Is this all that remains of so much effort, pain and sorrow?

I am drawn up in my dark imaginings. There must be

sweeter memories; there are. What about joy and love in kindly homes. The pain of travail giving way to joy of new life; notwithstanding the urgent worry of another mouth to feed.

There were lives nurtured and educated in the homes, as well as the school within guide lines that were soon accepted by children: that parents knew better what was best. Death was not an infrequent visitor, but it too had its bonding effect in the lives of the people.

There was also the prodigality of sharing in the middle of poverty; a helping hand was ready and willing in time of need.

There was humour where you would least expect it. Into its roughness were sewn threads of gentleness, so who will say it was only 'Dirty Highwid.' Insignificant it may be in the great history of our nation. Where will it fit into the culture and progress of the age? Is this an emblem to mans' adventure, or a fitting tombstone to his great exploits and achievements?

I am loath to leave the place under a heavy cloud. Suddenly there is a lightening in the sky, and soon the rain is over and gone: The sun broke through, scattering the clouds and mist with its own power. It was not newly created; I had been there all the time.

Slowly well known places shook themselves clear, as the sun warmed the air, and soon the hill range in the distance made a fitting background for the nearby villages of Tarbrax, Auchengray, Wilsontown and Forth that circled me.

I was standing that morning, not in a deserted village, but at the centre of the planet It was a lift to my spirit as well as warmth to my old bones.

I had arrived with a prayer on my lips. I left with a song in my heart.

There is hope

Robert L Aitken

FARMS 'ROON AUCHENGRAY'

There's Willie Dick in Viewfield
Just Knockin' oot his life
To mak' his ferm as muckle yield
As keep his weans and wife.

There's Red McCallum in Loanheed
Wha pays nae rent ava
But he's a wife and weans to feed
And that just tak's it a'.

There's Robertson's in Greenfield
Wi' family noo grown up
But Greenfield ferm could never yield
As much as they could sup.

The brothers Black in Easterhoose
Hae neither wives nor weans,
Bane ever heard them crawin' croose
Aboot their farming gains.

There's Thomas in Blackcastle
A hardy, shifty lot,
But wi' could land to wrastle
There's litte to be got.

John Struthers in Yardhouse
Rears first class sheep and kye
But after breeks and blouses
There's naething to put bye.

At Kings Inns noo we've Bob Dunlop
On him I canna speak
The chap's just newly started shop
And had nae time to squeak.

The Sanderson's in Gridwoodend
Hae reared a family too,
And they've been often pressed to fend
And bring the bairnies throo.

The Letham Brother's in Muirha'
Some think are richt for life,
We'el John may save a bob or twa
But Robin's got a wife.

The Hamilton's that farm the Pool
Slave on baith day and nicht,
In spite o't a' they canna pull
A fortune into light.

Tis Orr's that farm in Hardgateheid,
Some hae the healing gift,
And throo it they may yet succeed,
To gie farm stock a lift.

Mrs. Dunlop works hard to cope,
Wi' Hillhead, Auchengray,
But freen', there's cunco little hope
Wi' could wet moss and clay.

Auld Jimmy Dick Mid-Auchengray,
Has wrocht until he's bent,
And dressed in sackcloth every day
To keep to pay his rent.

At Benthead we hae Mrs. Dick
A hardy, able woman,
she afeast the ane that winna stick
but fortune ian in comin'.

There's Willie Barrie at Mosshat,
Can hardly get his meat
His socks are holed and gude kens what
Is wrangtwiset heid and feet.

There's Hamilton in Woolfords farm
His farmings never done
But like the rest he's failed to charm
A fortune oot the grun.

The Auctioneers o' Gorgie Market
Will make a tidy bit
Aff the Kye frae Easter Yardies
And the sheepfields o' Dykefuit.

Frae Adam Letham's o' Lawheed
Tae Walker's o' Blackhill
Tae Baillie's o' the Calla
Tae Byres'es o' Badsmill
Frae Sanderson's o' Girdwood
And doon by Ampherlaw
And a' the places roon aboot
I canna name them a'
They've a got something in their trade
That's earned for them their fame
So though Auchengray's a gye wee place
AT LEAST IT'S GOT A NAME.

GLOSSARY

bicker - complain or argue but going on
birky - sharp tongued quick tempered woman (usual)
bools - bowls - as in game
braw - beautiful
bunnett - bonnett or helmet
bykes - hives
carmudgen - irascible person
chapped - knocked
cheil - fellow
clokin - a broody hen
crabbit - cross
cruise - loudly confident - a cock crowing on its own dyke
darg - an allocated task
daunner roon - walk round
douce - sedate respectful pleasant and comfortable
fecht - fend or fight
fee - another place of employed
full fou and fetch mair - fill full and bring more
geikin - glowering
girn - complain - akin to
graith - tools
greitin - crying and sobbing

happit - covered
herried - rob a nest
het - one who chases in childrens games
huffed - upset and taking offence - silent
hurl - ride or carry
jant - jaunt
kinna - kind of
lousing - finishing
maskit - brewed
nabbery - gentry
parritch - porridge
pickle - a small amount
poussie - a faulty shot in which a marble is lobbed - not flicked
rickle - an emaciated broken person (rickle o'banes)
stravaiging - wandering
smout - small insignificant
sneck - latch
sook - one who curries favour
spelled - taking turns
tattie howkers - harversters of potato crop
tholing - bear or suffer
trig - posh
yince - once